Contents

Saving Lives: Our Healthier Nation

Presented to Parliament by the Secretary of State for Health
by Command of Her Majesty ~ July 1999

Cm 4386   £15

Foreword by the Prime Minister

Rt Hon Tony Blair MP

In our country today, too many people suffer from poor health. Too many people are ill for much of their lives. Too many people die too young from illnesses which are preventable.

But at the same time, many people realise the value of better health. Many already take exercise, eat properly, and don't smoke.

I believe that by working together, we can tackle poor health, and achieve the aim of better health for everyone, and especially for the least fortunate. To do that, we have to combat the key killers in our country - cancer, heart disease and stroke, accidents and mental illness.

Individuals taking action for themselves and their families are central to this. Communities working together can offer real help. And there is a vital role for Government too. Not as the so-called nanny state in action. But the Government addressing the big issues which affect our health, like housing, jobs and education.

This White Paper is a significant step towards better health. It sets out a new, modern approach to public health – an approach which refuses to accept that there is no role for anything other than individual improvement, or that only Government can do something. An approach which no Government in Britain has adopted before.

I am determined that New Labour in Government will meet what we see as our clear responsibilities, and play our part in improving the health of everyone in Britain.

Preface

This White Paper sets out how we propose to save lives, promote healthier living and reduce inequality in health.

That will require action by Government, by local organisations and by individuals. Some of the factors which harm people's health are beyond the control of any single individual. Like air pollution, unemployment, low wages, crime and disorder, poor housing. So, in co-operation with local councils, the NHS, and local voluntary bodies and businesses, the Government must take action.

And we are – right across the board. Tackling joblessness through the New Deal, ending low pay through the National Minimum Wage, improving housing by our housing investment and energy saving programmes, reducing crime and disorder, reducing air and noise pollution and through modern transport policies. And that has been achieved only by a co-operative effort right across Government. We reject the view that nothing can be done to improve the health of the worst off.

But individuals too have a responsibility for their own health. Everybody should try to look after themselves better, by not smoking, taking more exercise, eating and drinking sensibly. It's not the Government's job to tell people what to do. It is the Government's job to spell out the facts and quantify the risks on which individuals can make informed decisions.

We have to do that in a much more effective way and to target most effort on the people and places that need it most. Campaigns to improve health must concentrate on the least healthy.

Everyone in the country is affected by this programme and we have to do our best to make sure that everyone is committed to it. That's the only way we can get things done – saving lives, improving health and reducing inequality.

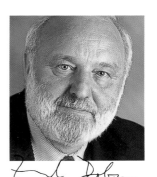

Frank Dobson
Department of Health

Tessa Jowell
Department of Health

Hugh Bayley
Department of Social Security

Patricia Hewitt
HM Treasury

Margaret Beckett
President of the Council

George Howarth
Home Office

Charles Clarke
Department for Education
and Employment

Kim Howells
Department of Trade
and Industry

Jeff Rooker
Ministry of Agriculture,
Fisheries and Food

Michael Meacher
Department of the Environment,
Transport and the Regions

Alan Meale
Department of the Environment,
Transport and the Regions

Clare Short
Department for International
Development

vii

Executive summary

Saving lives: Our Healthier Nation is an **action plan** to tackle poor health. We want to:

- improve the health of **everyone**
- and the health of the **worst off** in particular.

Good health is fundamental to all our lives. But too many people

- are ill for much of their lives
- die too young from **preventable** illness.

'the first comprehensive Government plan'

We are putting forward the **first comprehensive Government plan** focused on the main killers: **cancer, coronary heart disease and stroke, accidents, mental illness.**

We reject the previous Government's scattergun targets. Instead we are setting tougher but **attainable targets** in priority areas. **By the year 2010:**

- **CANCER:** to reduce the death rate in people under 75 **by at least a fifth**
- **CORONARY HEART DISEASE and STROKE:** to reduce the death rate in people under 75 **by at least two fifths**
- **ACCIDENTS:** to reduce the death rate by **at least a fifth** and serious injury **by at least a tenth**
- **MENTAL ILLNESS:** to reduce the death rate from suicide and undetermined injury **by at least a fifth.**

'tougher but attainable targets'

If we achieve these targets, we have the opportunity to save lives by preventing up to **300,000 untimely and unnecessary deaths.** To achieve **better health** for everyone and especially for the worst off we are:

- putting in **more money:** £21 billion for the NHS alone to help secure a healthier population
- tackling **smoking** as the single biggest preventable cause of poor health
- **integrating Government,** and local government, work to improve health

- stressing health improvement as a key role for the **NHS**
- pressing for **high health standards** for all, not just the privileged few.

In securing better health, we reject the old arguments of the past. We believe that:

- the **social, economic and environmental** factors tending towards poor health are potent
- people can make individual decisions about their and their families' health which can make a difference.

We want to see a new balance in which **people, communities and Government** work together in **partnership** to improve health. Our drive for better health is in line with a background of **real improvement** in health:

- people live **longer and healthier** lives
- **life expectancy** is now 80 for women and 75 for men
- many **infectious diseases** of the past – such as cholera, diphtheria and polio – have been brought under control
- death in **childbirth** is now rare.

But **new problems** arise, including AIDS and variant Creutzfeldt-Jakob disease.

People can improve their own health, through physical activity, better diet and quitting smoking. Individuals and their families need to be properly informed about risk to make decisions. We are introducing new **Healthy Citizens** programmes to help make decisions:

- *NHS Direct* – a nurse-led telephone helpline and Internet service providing information and advice on health
- **Health Skills** programmes for people to help themselves and others
- **Expert Patients** programmes to help people manage their own illnesses

'social, economic and environmental factors tending towards poor health are potent'

'people can make individual decisions about their and their families' health'

'tackling sexual health, drugs, alcohol, food safety, water fluoridation and communicable diseases'

Communities can tackle poor health, which springs too from a range of wider, **community factors** – including poverty, low wages, unemployment, poor education, sub-standard housing, crime and disorder and a polluted environment.

Health inequality is widespread: the **most disadvantaged** have suffered most from poor health. **The Government** is addressing inequality with a range of initiatives on education, welfare-to-work, housing, neighbourhoods, transport and the environment which will **help improve health.**

As well as **taking action** on our key targets, we are also tackling other important health issues like sexual health, drugs, alcohol, food safety, water fluoridation and communicable diseases – to put our new approach **into practice.**

We will **reorient the NHS** to ensure that for the first time ever, health improvement will be **integrated** into the local delivery of health care:

- **health authorities** have a new role in improving the health of local people
- **primary care groups and primary care trusts** have new responsibilities for public health.

Local authorities will work in partnership with the NHS to plan for health improvement:

- **health action zones** will break down barriers in providing services
- **healthy living centres** will provide help for better health.

'Local authorities will work in partnership with the NHS'

For partnership to work, public health will need **high standards,** and for public health to be improved, it will need **success measures.** On **standards,** we will:

- establish a new **Health Development Agency,** a statutory body charged with raising the standards and quality of public health provision
- increase **education and training for health,** with a new skills audit and workforce development plan, and **specific measures** for nurses, midwives, health visitors, school nurses and others

- review **public health information**, establish public health observatories in each NHS region, set up disease registers, and promote **research**

- establish a new *Public Health Development Fund.*

On **success measures**, we will:

- chart progress through **interim milestones** in the four priority areas to demonstrate how far we have got towards our targets by 2005
- require **local targets** for improving health
- **manage performance** through the new NHS performance assessment framework.

We want to see **healthier people in a healthier country. People** improving their own health supported by **communities** working through local organisations against a backdrop of action by the **Government.**

We want to see everyone take the opportunity of **better health – now, and for the future.**

'take the opportunity of better health'

Initiatives in this White Paper

Where to find details of:

Liam Donaldson
Chief Medical Officer

Ten Tips For Better Health

1 Don't smoke. If you can, stop. If you can't, cut down.

2 Follow a balanced diet with plenty of fruit and vegetables.

3 Keep physically active.

4 Manage stress by, for example, talking things through and making time to relax.

5 If you drink alcohol, do so in moderation.

6 Cover up in the sun, and protect children from sunburn.

7 Practise safer sex.

8 Take up cancer screening opportunities.

9 Be safe on the roads: follow the Highway Code.

10 Learn the First Aid ABC - airways, breathing, circulation.

1 Better health: a new approach

1.1 England is a rich country - rich in its people, rich in its resources, rich in innovation, rich in its values, rich in its history, rich in its future. Yet in this rich country, not everyone has an equal chance of healthy life. Too many people suffer from poor health. Too many people are ill for much of their lives. Too many people die too young from preventable diseases.

1.2 *Saving lives: Our Healthier Nation* is an action plan for tackling poor health and improving the health of everyone in England, especially the worst off.

1.3 We believe that if we can achieve the bold objectives we are setting we have the opportunity of saving as many as 300,000 lives over the next 10 years.

1.4 But to do that, we have to tackle the four main killers – the illnesses which, together with accidents, play the greatest part in causing preventable deaths and ill-health: cancer, coronary heart disease and stroke and mental illness. Together they account for

'the opportunity of saving as many as 300,000 lives'

more than 75 per cent of all the people who die before the age of 75 years. Combating these killers will not end them: they will still cut into people's lives and the lives of their families. But we can reduce their impact.

'We will achieve what no previous Government has achieved'

1.5 So we are setting new, tougher and challenging targets in each of these priority areas. By 2010:

- **Cancer**
  to reduce the death rate from cancer in people under 75 by at least a fifth – saving 100,000 lives

- **Coronary heart disease and stroke**
  to reduce the death rate from coronary heart disease and stroke and related diseases in people under 75 by at least two fifths – saving 200,000 lives

- **Accidents**
  to reduce the death rate from accidents by at least a fifth and to reduce the rate of serious injury from accidents by at least a tenth – saving 12,000 lives

- **Mental health**
  to reduce the death rate from suicide and undetermined injury by at least a fifth – saving 4,000 lives

1.6 These are ambitious targets. But they are achievable – and we are committing ourselves to make steady progress towards achieving them.

1.7 We believe we can succeed in this ambition. We believe we can make a difference. We have the principles and programmes in place which will achieve what no previous Government has achieved:

- **Funding.** We are investing more money than ever before in encouraging a healthier population. Up to £110 million into helping people give up smoking. £300 million through the National Lottery into healthy living centres. £290 million into health action zones. £54 million into *NHS Direct*. And an extra £96 million to support the implementation of this White

Paper through a new *Public Health Development Fund.*
These specific areas of investment are underpinned by the
extra £21 billion on health which we made available through
the Comprehensive Spending Review.

- **Integration.** We believe in working across Government to
attack the breeding ground of poor health – poverty and social
exclusion – and we believe in creating strong local partnerships
with local authorities, health authorities and other agencies to
tackle the root causes of ill-health in places where people live.

- **Standards.** We believe in high standards for all, not just a
privileged few. We believe that good health, like good education,
should be within reach of all. Government should help people
to achieve it and in turn individuals have a responsibility to do
all they can to live a healthy life.

- **Health service.** We are re-activating a dormant duty of the
NHS – to promote good health, not just treat people when
they fall sick. That means a new role for primary care staff;
improved screening services; better co-ordinated health
research; a stronger public health workforce; new local
initiatives – including the revolutionary *NHS Direct* which
will provide rapid access to information and help for the
entire population.

- **New public health.** We are establishing a Health Development
Agency to ensure that organisations and individual practitioners
build their work on the highest standards and raise the quality
of public health in England.

- **Smoking.** Unlike previous Governments we believe in tackling
head on the single biggest preventable cause of poor health.

1.8 These are the building blocks for our new policy for improving
the health of our population. They require individuals,
communities, local organisations and Government to contribute
to meeting the targets in a three-way partnership. Better health is
the prize.

'to attack the breeding ground of poor health – poverty and social exclusion'

'good health, like good education, should be within reach of all'

3

'If people are healthier, their demands on the health service will be less than they would have been'

Better health

1.9 Good health is fundamental to all our lives. We all treasure our own health, and the health of our families and friends. Good health is the bedrock on which we build strong families, strong communities and a strong country.

1.10 When we enjoy good health, we are able to make the most of the opportunities life has to offer. We can play a full part in our working lives, our family lives and our community lives. Nothing is more precious to most of us than our health.

1.11 Yet we tend to take health for granted – until something goes wrong. Then we look for help – to doctors, to nurses and to hospitals. In Government we are determined to make the modern NHS ready and able to respond to what people need from it.

1.12 But the better everyone's health is, the greater the ability of the NHS to use its resources to best effect. If people are healthier, their demands on the health service will be less than they would have been – leaving resources and facilities available for those who need them more.

1.13 Improving health is about more than just treating people when they become ill. Better health is vital in itself, leading directly to longer, more active and more fulfilled lives.

1.14 Many people are already taking the initiative to safeguard and improve their health. They are increasingly aware of the importance of a better diet, of the value of physical activity, of the benefits of taking proper care of themselves and their families. The enthusiasm of many for improving their health is clearly reflected in the increased levels of informal physical activity such as walking and keeping fit, as well as the use of fitness and sports centres. Support for health is also reflected in the growth of complementary therapies and specialist products, including magazines, radio and television programmes and health websites, for people wanting to improving their health.

1.15 Better health is central to economic performance. A healthier workforce improves productivity and performance. In 1995 in

Great Britain around 20 million working days were lost through work-related ill-health. Ill-health is expensive in both economic and human terms. Cutting the cost of sickness at work will help to decrease burdens on business. As we understand more about the causes of disease, such as coronary heart disease, so we can act to reduce preventable illness. And that has the potential to reduce welfare spending as we tackle health inequality and improve the health of the worst off.

'Cutting the cost of sickness at work will help to decrease burdens on business'

1.16 A modern and successful country needs more people in better health. We are engaged in a wide-ranging programme of modernisation: modernising education, modernising welfare, modernising social services and, in *The new NHS* White Paper, modernising the National Health Service. A modern approach to improving health and closing the health gap is a key part of this programme.

1.17 Our modern approach is reflected in the goals of this White Paper:

- to improve the health of the population as a whole by increasing the length of people's lives and the number of years people spend free from illness; and

- to improve the health of the worst off in society and to narrow the health gap.

1.18 Our twin goals are consistent with the health strategies being adopted by the other countries of the United Kingdom. They are also consistent with the World Health Organisation (Europe)'s new programme for the 21st Century *Health 21* and the European Community's developing strategy for public health.

1.19 We propose the first comprehensive Government plan focused on the main killers of people in our country. We are determined to succeed in our goals – and if we do, then by cutting needless early deaths from cancer, coronary heart disease and stroke, accidents and suicide, there is the real prospect of reducing the number of deaths from these causes by up to 300,000 by the year 2010.

1.20 This is a bold ambition. Improving health for all and tackling health inequality is a challenging objective – a crusade for health on a scale never undertaken by Government before. We will

measure the success of our ambition by the numbers of lives saved, and by the improvement in the health of the people of our country. The task is clear: to give everyone in our nation, whatever their background, the chance to lead a long and healthy life.

The way to better health

1.21 Improving health means tackling the causes of poor health. We know that the causes of ill-health are many: a complex interaction between personal, social, economic and environmental factors.

1.22 In our new approach to better health, we want to break with the past. We want to move beyond the old arguments and tired debates which have characterised so much consideration of public health issues, including those who say that nothing can be done to improve the health of the poorest, and those who say that individuals are solely to blame for their own ill-health.

1.23 These arguments have focused not on what can be achieved, but on what role there is for those involved – including whether there is a role for Government, or whether these matters are solely issues of personal responsibility.

1.24 We reject the polarity of these positions. We refuse to accept that there is no role for anything other than the personal. Equally we refuse to accept that for some people poor health is inevitable.

1.25 We reject that hopelessness. As with our policies on education and employment, we reject the inevitability of wasted lives and wasted generations – the belief that nothing can be done. As with education and employment, we believe that people can be instrumental in shaping their own futures, rather than being victims of them. And there is a clear role for local agencies acting together, offering help with the decisions that individuals make.

1.26 People are responsible for their own actions in health as in other areas. But the decisions people take over their health are more likely to result in better health and a healthier life if they have the opportunity to make informed decisions.

'We refuse to accept that there is no role for anything other than the personal. Equally we refuse to accept that for some people poor health is inevitable'

6

1.27 Our new approach is rooted in precisely that balance. We believe that individuals can, should and do affect how healthy they are. But we believe too that there are powerful factors beyond the control of the individual which can harm health. The Government has a clear responsibility to address these fundamental problems. Striking a new balance – a third way – linking individual and wider action is at the heart of our new approach.

1.28 Smoking provides a striking example of these various factors at work. We have set out our policy on smoking in our White Paper on tobacco, *Smoking Kills.* Smoking is the most powerful factor which determines whether people live beyond middle age. And smoking more than any other identifiable factor contributes to the gap in healthy life expectancy between the most deprived and the most advantaged. But it is at the same time a factor about which individuals can make a decision. For many people who smoke, the decision to give up is not an easy one. Nicotine is addictive. But there is a clear route to better health. It is a clear route too which those who are more fortunate tend to take more than those who are less fortunate. We want people to stop smoking. But we also want that policy to have a greater impact among the less fortunate, where the harm caused by smoking is greater. To do that we have to address the complex interactions of social, economic and personal factors. Tackling smoking achieves both our objectives – improved health for all, and especially better health for the worse off.

1.29 For people to make such decisions against the background of such powerful determinants, they need to make informed decisions. Such decisions must be based on information about the risks involved in a range of activities, practices and products. People cannot and should not be pressured into responsibility. We do not believe in the old nanny-state approach. But there is a powerful role for Government in making clear the nature and scale of risk, and in some cases, taking protective action in the light of it.

1.30 We recognise that this is an unusual area for Government action. Governments can set the preconditions for success in improving health. But Governments alone cannot determine success. To do that, the Government needs to work in partnership with others.

'a new balance – a third way – linking individual and wider action'

'Governments can set the preconditions for success in improving health. But Governments cannot determine success'

A three-way partnership

1.31 Partnership is a key element of the Government's approach to a wide range of issues. Partnerships in areas such as business, education, crime prevention and many others are at the core of the way the Government carries out its work. Partnership is at the heart of our new approach to better health in *Saving lives: Our Healthier Nation*.

1.32 To improve health and to tackle health inequality, we need a new three-way partnership, comprising:

- individuals

- communities

- Government

'a new three-way partnership, comprising: individuals, communities, and Government'

1.33 **Individuals** are central to our new vision for better health. People need to take responsibility for their own health – and many are doing so. There is a new and clear realisation that individuals can improve their health, by what they do and the actions they take.

1.34 Better health information – and the means of applying that information – is the bedrock on which improvements to the health of individuals will be made. But better health opportunities and decisions are not easily available to everyone. For example, membership of a gym may not be an option for someone in a poor neighbourhood or a single mother.

1.35 **Communities** working in partnership through local organisations are the best means of delivering the better information, better services and better community-wide programmes which will lead to better health. The roles of the NHS and of local authorities are crucial. They must become organisations for health improvement, as well as for health care and service provision. We are underlining this joint responsibility by the new duty of partnership on NHS bodies and local government in the Health Act. All aspects of the way that the NHS works with other local bodies, from the reorganisation of primary care services to the development of healthy neighbourhoods, from the *NHS Direct* phone-line to the creation of a new Health Development Agency, will be geared not just to treatment of illness but to the prevention and early detection of ill-health.

1.36 Initiatives including the *Healthy Citizens* programme, health improvement programmes and health action zones will all provide a local focus for the delivery of information and programmes at local level aimed at helping individuals improve their health and the health of their families. The dynamic of health improvement will for the first time be integrated into the local delivery of health care.

1.37 **Government** will play its part by creating the right conditions for individuals to make healthy decisions. Across a range of Government policy, we are focusing on the factors that increase the likelihood of poor health – poor housing, poverty, unemployment, crime, poor education and family breakdown.

1.38 The Government is taking action to combat social exclusion, to make work pay, to support children and families, to promote community safety – all moves which will do much to improve people's health, and to improve especially the health of the least fortunate in our country.

'creating the right conditions for individuals to make healthy decisions'

An integrated approach

1.39 This is our new contract for health. Our new approach, based on our three-way partnership between people, local communities and the Government, adopts a new way of tackling poor health which is both inclusive and integrated, comprehensive and coherent.

1.40 It ensures that all involved in improving health play their part. Individuals have the responsibility to improve their health, and the health of their families. Local agencies, led by health and local authorities, have the responsibility for delivering local services and local programmes which will enable people to claim the right of better health. And the Government has the responsibility of giving everyone throughout our country the opportunity for better education, better housing, and better prospects of securing work.

'the whole will be greater than the sum of the parts'

1.41 Common sense suggests that this integrated approach to tackling poor health is best. It is supported by the scientific and medical evidence. Reducing the impact of cancer and heart disease, for example, can be done only if we tackle smoking effectively. In turn, tackling smoking depends on relieving the conditions – social stress, unemployment, poor education, crime, vandalism – which lead far more people in disadvantaged communities to smoke than in other sections of the community.

1.42 Our approach, based on partnership between individuals, communities and Government, is not one which ranks action by one above the other: by emphasising integration our strategy will ensure that the whole will be greater than the sum of the parts.

Targets

1.43 Previous efforts to try to address poor health have been marred both by the limited nature of their approach, resting on simplistic explanations of the causes of ill-health rather than the approach to root causes which we are adopting, and by an over-reliance on too many, poorly focused priorities.

1.44 We will not fall prey to these failings. We reject the checklist approach to improving public health. Instead, we are identifying tough but realistic targets which concentrate on the most important killers of people across our nation:

- cancer

- coronary heart disease and stroke

- accidents

- suicide

Listening and learning

1.45 Ten months after coming into office, we set out the scale of the challenge for improving health and tackling health inequality in

England in our Green Paper, *Our Healthier Nation*. Over 5,500 responses were received. The response to consultation was overwhelmingly supportive with well over 90 per cent in favour of the proposed approach.

1.46 Individuals and organisations who responded particularly welcomed the emphasis on the fundamental social, economic and environmental causes of ill-health. They also approved of the much wider approach to accountability for improving health which identified the respective roles and responsibilities of individuals, local organisations and Government for improving health.

1.47 We commissioned Sir Donald Acheson to carry out an Independent Inquiry into Inequalities in Health to review the position and to identify the most critical areas to tackle.

1.48 We also commissioned an important study of the previous Government's health policy *The Health of the Nation*, carried out by specialists from the Universities of Leeds and Glamorgan and the London School of Hygiene and Tropical Medicine. Its findings have helped to shape this strategy.

OUR
HEALTHIER
NATION

A Contract for Health
A Consultation Paper

Our Healthier Nation

1.49 We believe that the country is united in an ambition for better health. The ambition to bring up children so that they grow up healthy is one that unites us all. The ambition of a long and healthy life for ourselves unites us all.

1.50 The three-way partnership we see as vital to improving our health is reflected in this White Paper:

- **Our Healthier Nation** – our approach to the causes of poor health (chapters 1-4)

- **saving lives** – the ways to tackle our priority areas of cancer, coronary heart disease and stroke, accidents and mental health (chapters 5-9)

- **making it work** – how we will ensure that our approach operates in practice (chapters 10-11)

1.51 This partnership approach underpins the contracts for health, set out in succeeding chapters, which summarise the action to be taken at each level – individual, local agencies, Government – to tackle each of the most important killers.

'action to tackle the four big killers'

1.52 We want to see healthier people in a healthier country. We want to see individuals striving to improve their own health, supported by local organisations working in partnership to deliver the information and services they need, against a backdrop of action by the Government. We want to see people deciding for themselves that they want to embrace better health – but doing so in the light of real and trusted information about the benefits, and about any risks. We will do so by providing the help which was so lacking in the past; and above all we will make it available to the least fortunate. We believe that this holds out the prospect of better health for everyone. We want to see everyone take the chance – and seize better health now, and for the future.

2 Public health: aims and advances

2.1 Central to our action programme for improving health, particularly for the most disadvantaged, is tackling these killers – cancer, coronary heart disease and stroke, accidents and mental ill-health. Not everyone who is touched by them dies. Many recover, and go on to resume normal lives. But the death rate from our four priority areas of ill-health is unacceptably high. And for those who do not die, the impact of long-term illness is dramatic – for them and for the people around them. We are determined to see the impact of these key killers reduced.

'we stand on the threshold of the 21st Century'

2.2 These four priority areas stand out increasingly starkly from the map showing the progress made in recent times in combating disease and illness. As we stand on the threshold of the 21st Century we can look back over more than a thousand years of struggle against the killer diseases of the past which brought early death, disease and misery to millions of people in cities and countries around the world:

- a third of the population of Europe and Asia lost to bubonic plague in the 14th Century

- the epidemic of cholera which descended on Victorian England leaving tens of thousands dead in its wake mainly in the towns and cities of the industrial revolution

- childbirth often not survived by mother or child.

2.3 We can take heart from the advances which have been made. Many of the infectious diseases which caused such devastation in the past – cholera, diphtheria, polio – have been brought under control. If we are vigilant they should not return.

'dramatic improvements in health will continue'

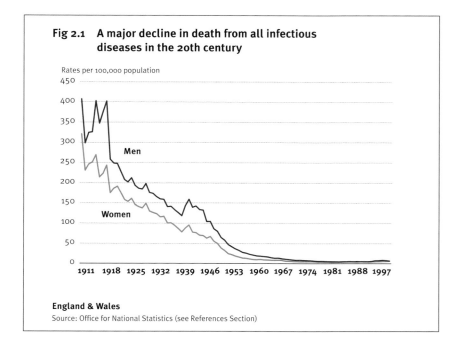

Fig 2.1 A major decline in death from all infectious diseases in the 20th century

Rates per 100,000 population

England & Wales
Source: Office for National Statistics (see References Section)

2.4 The dramatic improvements in health seen during the present century will continue into the next. We now live longer and healthier lives. Survival into old age is commonplace. Life expectancy is currently 80 for women and 75 for men compared with 48 and 44 in 1900.

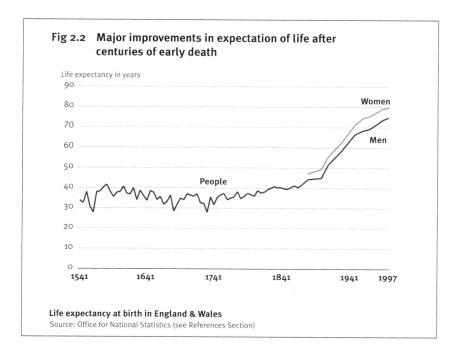

Fig 2.2 Major improvements in expectation of life after centuries of early death

Life expectancy in years

Life expectancy at birth in England & Wales
Source: Office for National Statistics (see References Section)

2.5 Death in childbirth is now rare. Infant deaths in the first year of
life have fallen from more than 100 in every 1,000 to only 6.
Children's funerals, such a feature of even the recent past, are
now an infrequent sight.

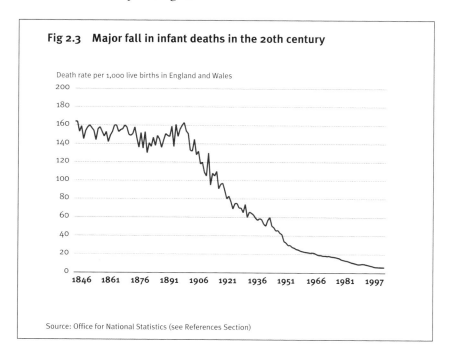

Fig 2.3 Major fall in infant deaths in the 20th century

Death rate per 1,000 live births in England and Wales

Source: Office for National Statistics (see References Section)

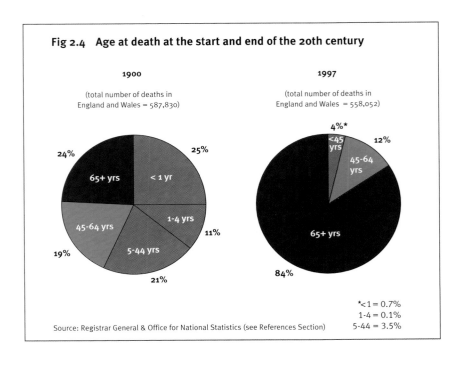

Fig 2.4 Age at death at the start and end of the 20th century

1900
(total number of deaths in England and Wales = 587,830)

1997
(total number of deaths in England and Wales = 558,052)

*<1 = 0.7%
1-4 = 0.1%
5-44 = 3.5%

Source: Registrar General & Office for National Statistics (see References Section)

Today's problems

'new health problems have emerged'

2.6 But against this background of overall improvement and optimism, new health problems have emerged and others have increased in importance. Formidable challenges remain. We may have won many battles against deadly infectious diseases of the past, but some, like tuberculosis, are rising again. And new threats – like AIDS and variant Creutzfeldt-Jakob disease – have emerged, causing human tragedies.

2.7 What is more, we are experiencing epidemics of health problems which were less prominent in the past. Cancer, coronary heart disease and stroke are our modern-day killer diseases. Together with accidental injury and mental illness they are prominent features of the health profile of the population of our country in the late 1990s.

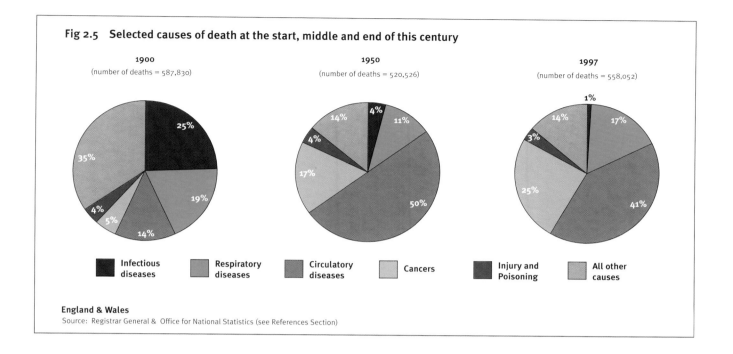

Fig 2.5   Selected causes of death at the start, middle and end of this century

1900
(number of deaths = 587,830)

1950
(number of deaths = 520,526)

1997
(number of deaths = 558,052)

| Infectious diseases | Respiratory diseases | Circulatory diseases | Cancers | Injury and Poisoning | All other causes |

England & Wales
Source: Registrar General & Office for National Statistics (see References Section)

2.8 Cancer

Years of life lost

- at current rates about one in four (25 per cent) of us will die from cancer, which is responsible for 127,000 deaths every year

- a third of all cancer deaths, and between 80 and 90 per cent of deaths from lung cancer, are caused by smoking

- one fifth of cancer deaths in women are due to breast cancer

Years of health lost

- approximately 200,000 cases of cancer are diagnosed in England each year

- more than one third of us will suffer from cancer during our lifetime

- about one fifth of cancer cases are cancer of the lung

- nearly one third of cancer cases in women are breast cancer

'more than one third of us will suffer from cancer'

Health disadvantage

- 40 per cent of unskilled men smoke compared with 12 per cent of men in professional jobs

- Bangladeshi women are less than half as likely as other women in this country to come forward for cervical screening

Counting the cost

- cancer accounts for as much as £1 billion each year of NHS hospital expenditure

- by achieving our target there would be up to 100,000 fewer deaths from this cause over the period to 2010 – more than 60,000 through primary prevention and approximately 20,000 each through better screening and treatment

2.9 Coronary heart disease and stroke

Years of life lost

- coronary heart disease is one of the biggest single causes of death – causing almost 115,000 deaths each year in England

- about a quarter of people who suffer a heart attack die before they are admitted to hospital

- stroke is one of the main causes of death – it caused over 54,000 deaths in 1997, almost 12,500 in people under the age of 75 years.

- coronary heart disease, stroke and related diseases combined were responsible for 41 per cent of all deaths in 1997

- coronary heart disease is responsible for a total loss each year of over 1.25 million years of life before the age of 75 years in England

Years of health lost

- coronary heart disease is an important cause of disability – one in every twenty people reporting serious disability identifies coronary heart disease as a cause

'heart disease is one of the biggest single causes of death'

- stroke is also one of the leading causes of disability – one person in every 14 of those reporting serious disability identifies stroke as a cause

- coronary heart disease accounts for 2 million hospital bed-days per year

- stroke accounts for another 2 million hospital bed-days per year

Health disadvantage

- the death rate from coronary heart disease in people aged under 65 years is almost three times higher in Manchester than in Kingston and Richmond

- death rates for coronary heart disease for those born in the Indian sub-continent are 38 per cent higher for men and 43 per cent higher for women than rates for the country as a whole

- the death rate from coronary heart disease is now 3 times higher among unskilled men than among professionals and the gap has widened sharply in the last 20 years.

- stroke death rates in people born in the Caribbean and the Indian sub-continent are one and a half to two and a half times higher than for people born in this country – a differential that has persisted from the late 1970s

'the death rate from coronary heart disease is now 3 times higher among unskilled men'

Counting the cost

- coronary heart disease accounts for more than $2^{1}/_{2}$ per cent of NHS hospital expenditure and almost 2 per cent of NHS primary care expenditure

- stroke accounts for more than 4 per cent of NHS expenditure

- stroke is the second most important cause of expenditure on community health and social care for adults – accounting for over 7 per cent of such expenditure

2.10 Accidents

Years of life lost

- accidents claim over 10,000 lives per year

- nearly one third of deaths in 10-14 year olds are from accidental injury

- two thirds of accidental deaths among 15-24 year olds are due to road accidents

- every year more than 3,000 people aged 65 years and over die from falls

Years of health lost

- in one recent year there were 110,000 episodes of care in NHS hospitals solely because of unintentional injury in children aged under 15 years

- about 14 per cent of children consulted their general practitioner during the course of a single year about problems related to accidents and injury

Health disadvantage

- children up to the age of 15 years from unskilled families are 5 times more likely to die from unintentional injury than those from professional families

- children up to age 15 years from unskilled families are 15 times more likely to die in a fire in the home than those from professional families

- the rates of fatal accidents for 15-24 year-olds are higher in rural than in urban areas.

Counting the cost

- the NHS spends an estimated £1.6 billion every year to treat injury

- accidents in the home cost the country almost £30 billion a year

- the total value to the country of avoiding a single road accident death is estimated at almost £900,000

'the NHS spends £1.6 billion every year to treat injury'

2.11 Mental health

Years of life lost

- suicide and undetermined injury cause 4,500 deaths every year

- suicide accounts for 400,000 years of life lost before age 75 years

- suicide is the leading cause of death among men aged 15-24 years and the second most common cause of death among people aged under 35 years

- over 95 per cent of those who commit suicide had been suffering from mental illness before their death

- 10-15 per cent of people with severe mental illness kill themselves

- people with mental illness are also at increased risk of dying early from respiratory illness, cancer and coronary heart disease

Years of health lost

- 16 per cent of the adult population suffers from a common mental disorder such as depression or anxiety

- 12 per cent of children and adolescents suffer from a conduct or emotional disorder

- 30 per cent of people over 85 years suffer from dementia

- four people in every 1,000 suffer from a psychotic disorder such as schizophrenia

Health disadvantage

- women are more likely than men to seek help for a mental health problem

- suicide is three times more common in men than in women

- women living in England born in India and East Africa have 40 per cent higher suicide rates than those born here

- men in unskilled occupations are four times more likely to commit suicide than those in professional work

'over 95 per cent of those who commit suicide had been suffering from mental illness before their death'

Counting the cost

- treating mental illness costs the NHS and social services an estimated £7.5 billion every year

- people with mental illness have increased sickness absence, change jobs more often and are more likely to be unemployed

More years of health

2.12 Combating cancer, coronary heart disease and stroke, accidents and mental ill-health will help reduce needless early deaths, reduce suffering and allow people to live longer lives.

'People want to enjoy their extra years as healthy active years'

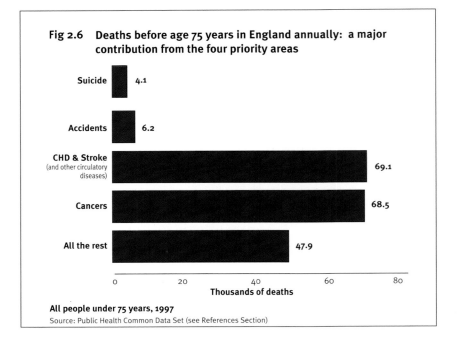

Fig 2.6   Deaths before age 75 years in England annually: a major contribution from the four priority areas

Suicide	4.1
Accidents	6.2
CHD & Stroke (and other circulatory diseases)	69.1
Cancers	68.5
All the rest	47.9

Thousands of deaths

All people under 75 years, 1997

Source: Public Health Common Data Set (see References Section)

2.13 But living longer lives is not enough. People want to enjoy their extra years as healthy active years. At present, men's average life expectancy of some 75 years will on average include 15 years of longstanding illness or disability. For women the picture is similar: they will spend 17 years out of 80 in some degree of ill-health. We want to see as many as possible of those years of illness turned into extra years of healthy active life.

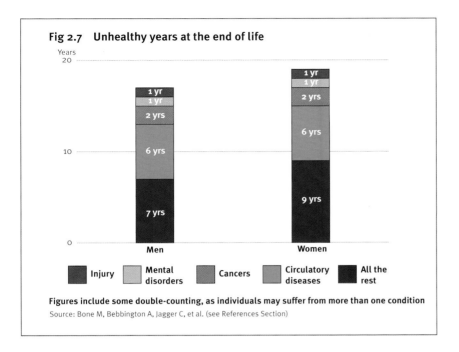

Fig 2.7   Unhealthy years at the end of life

Injury | Mental disorders | Cancers | Circulatory diseases | All the rest

Figures include some double-counting, as individuals may suffer from more than one condition

Source: Bone M, Bebbington A, Jagger C, et al. (see References Section)

2.14 To do all that, we need to tackle the complex causes of ill-health – causes in individuals' own lives, and in wider community issues. The two go hand in hand in our new approach to better health.

3 Individuals and health

3.1 How people live their lives – what they eat, how active they are, whether they smoke – is central to improving health. Other factors, including people's education, employment, housing and environment also play a key role.

3.2 Past health strategies have tended to focus excessively on lifestyle issues. Yet paradoxically they have often failed to recognise how people can play a positive part in building healthy lives for themselves and in contributing to the health of other members of society. People were treated as passive recipients of information and services, rather than as active partners. This contributed to the widening of the health gap: we now know that the better off are more likely to act on health information to change behaviour and reduce the risks to their health.

3.3 We know too that people with long-term health problems such as diabetes, epilepsy or arthritis are skilled at recognising the warning signs when their symptoms are getting worse or they need further treatment. In the past, services have not always been flexible enough to enable such people to play an active part in the management of their condition. As a result, people have had to wait to be seen and have become more dependent on health services than was necessary.

3.4 The Government recognises the importance of individuals making their own decisions about their own and their families' health. But we also believe that there are steps we can take to help support the decisions people make.

INDIVIDUALS AND HEALTH

Physical activity and health

3.5 People know that physical activity is one of the key determinants of good health. A physically active lifestyle, including walking, cycling or participating in sport, reduces the risk of coronary heart disease and stroke and promotes good mental health. The marked growth in the number of people taking part in sporting activities – whether formal or informal, whether with others or alone – is a significant feature of life for many people now, and one which the Government strongly supports.

3.6 To help support the enthusiasm for physical activity and for better health, we will publish a *sports strategy* later this year which will promote greater scope for participation in sport and physical activity for all. It will build on many existing initiatives:

- wide-ranging and affordable sports and leisure opportunities at local neighbourhood level

- *Exercise on prescription* where family doctors refer patients for physical activity courses as a cost-effective alternative to prescribing long-term medication

- specific sports programmes to encourage activity among people with such conditions as stress, obesity, or diabetes.

Physical activity

By not doing the recommended levels of physical activity –
30 minutes of moderate exercise
5 times each week – you are at:

- twice the risk of getting coronary heart disease

- three times the risk of suffering a stroke.

Diet and health

3.7   Diet is central to our health throughout life. A good diet during pregnancy is important for the healthy development of the growing baby. And women who breastfeed give their children the best start in life. A balanced diet during childhood helps to ensure that children grow well and do not become overweight as they get older. Avoiding sugary foods and drinks helps to prevent tooth decay. Good nutrition through adult life, with plenty of fruit and vegetables, cereals, and not too much fatty and salty food, will help to protect against coronary heart disease and stroke and some cancers. Taken together with physical activity a healthy diet enhances not just the length but also the quality of life.

3.8   People living in deprived neighbourhoods, where comparatively few people own cars and public transport is often poor, and people living in remoter rural areas, have most difficulty in reaching those shops which sell a range of affordable foods to make up a healthy and balanced diet. These "food deserts" can increase a sense of social exclusion and widen health inequality. Shopping at small independent cornershops can be as much as 60 per cent more expensive than a supermarket. As a result, the poorest people often face the highest prices. So one of the Policy Action Teams flowing from the Social Exclusion Unit's work on neighbourhood renewal is developing a strategy to improve shopping access for people living in deprived neighbourhoods. Its approach will foster and underpin the provision of local shops and services to meet everyday needs and, as a part of this, should make a balanced and healthy diet more readily available to these communities.

Smoking and health

3.9 Smoking is the single greatest cause of avoidable illness and preventable death in this country. And although most people now know the health risks of smoking, including from passive smoking, the decline in adult smoking rates since 1972 now appears to have halted, and may indeed have reversed. More worryingly, increasing numbers of children are starting to smoke.

3.10 In later chapters we show how important tackling smoking is to the reductions we are seeking in premature deaths and avoidable ill-health. If we are to achieve our targets more action is needed. In our White Paper *Smoking Kills* we set out a major action plan for tackling smoking, including ending tobacco advertising and providing new services to help people to give up.

Smoking

For every 1,000 20-year old smokers it is estimated that one will be murdered and six will die in motor accidents, but 250 will die in middle age from smoking, and another 250 will die in older age from smoking.

People: stress and health

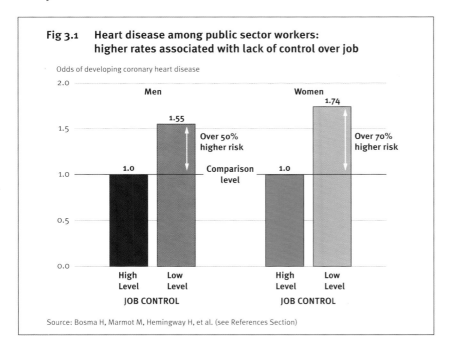

Fig 3.1   Heart disease among public sector workers: higher rates associated with lack of control over job

Odds of developing coronary heart disease

Men — High Level Job Control: 1.0; Low Level Job Control: 1.55 — Over 50% higher risk

Women — High Level Job Control: 1.0; Low Level Job Control: 1.74 — Over 70% higher risk

Comparison level

Source: Bosma H, Marmot M, Hemingway H, et al. (see References Section)

3.11 Stress can harm people's physical health. Evidence has shown that working in jobs which make very high demands, or in which people have little or no control, increases the risk of coronary heart disease and of premature death. Inadequate social support or lack of social networks can also have a harmful effect on health and on the chances of recovering from disease.

3.12 People can deal with stress in a number of ways, for example by relaxing, taking up creative pursuits, and being more physically active. Keeping in touch with friends and family and asking for help when necessary also helps. Government and others at national and local level can tackle the wider determinants of stress, for example by improving housing and the environment in general, by tackling poverty and unemployment and by managing stress at work.

Mothers and young children

'patterns of ill-health flow down the generations'

3.13 People's health can be strongly influenced by patterns of ill-health which can flow down the generations. For mothers and young children, the importance of improving health to break these patterns is clear. *Sure Start*, our new cross-Government programme, will provide support to parents and local communities, addressing their needs and making available the support they require to give their children the best possible start in life. It will be targeted on areas of need, providing the glue to bind together existing services, and enhance them to meet the particular needs of young families in the local community. More than £450 million will go into 250 local programmes in England, focused on children under four and their families.

'Sure Start works across the boundaries of Government departments'

3.14 *Sure Start* works across the boundaries of Government departments. In communities, it is multi-disciplinary, and multi-agency. *Sure Start* will build on good practice and local innovation, providing the extra resources needed to co-ordinate one-off projects and fill in any remaining gaps in service provision. It will help children begin school ready to thrive.

Communicating risk

3.15 Every day people are faced with decisions in their daily lives, including decisions which affect their health. Sometimes they recognise that certain decisions put their health at greater risk than others. But it is not always clear how great or small a risk they are taking.

3.16 We can help people to understand better about risk. Driving a car is a daily necessity for many, playing sport an occasional pleasure, and eating a plate of shellfish from a roadside caravan a personal preference. All, however, can carry risks of death, injury or acute illness. Armed with knowledge and information about risk, and being aware of the conditions under which risks can be greater, people can make informed decisions in managing their everyday life.

3.17 There are other potential risks to health where individuals expect Government or other responsible bodies to ensure that measures are in place to protect their health. For example, people expect to have a safe supply of pure drinking water; they do not expect a fast food restaurant to serve them partially cooked frozen chicken; and they do not consider it their responsibility to check that a train in which they are about to travel will be operated by a properly trained and competent driver.

3.18 There are still other risks to health where the public accepts that there is a need for more than passive release of information to allow them to make a decision. For example, in areas where lifestyle can affect health – HIV and AIDS, cigarette smoking, use of medicines in pregnancy – most people will expect the Government to have an active programme of education to explain the risks and advise the individual on the action to be taken to avoid them. They will also expect special efforts to be made in relation to children, young people, and those who are vulnerable or at particularly high risk.

'a better understanding of risks'

'a new relationship between Government and the public in relation to risk'

3.19 The whole question of risks to health, how they are analysed, assessed, communicated and reduced, has come to the fore during the 1990s. Many of the controversies have been in relation to food safety – the BSE crisis, the use of growth-promoting agents or antibiotics in animal farming. We need also to deal with those areas where people perceive possible risks to health but for which there is no scientific evidence of harm (from, for example, genetically modified foods or exposure to electro-magnetic fields). There have been other areas too. The risks of medicines such as the oral contraceptive pill, the perceived risks of vaccines, the risks of contracting meningitis have all captured the attention of the public and the media, often for weeks at a time. They have also highlighted the need for a new relationship between Government and the public in relation to risk.

3.20 We are currently reviewing our approach to risk and its communication. A series of seminars have involved key Ministers, the Better Regulation Task Force, senior officials, scientists, professionals, consumer representatives and journalists. The Task Force plans to make a series of recommendations as a result of these consultations.

3.21 In this White Paper we set out our approach to risk in relation to health. The areas of risk which can impact on health are many and varied, including:

- Environmental and other external hazards – such as radiation, or exhaust emissions

- Harm to the unborn baby – such as smoking in pregnancy

- Micro-organisms – such as Salmonella food poisoning

- Personal lifestyle – such as smoking, causing coronary heart disease and cancer

- Adverse outcomes of medical care – such as side-effects of medicines

- Sub-optimal outcomes of medical care – such as failure to prevent blindness in diabetes mellitus

- Errors in diagnosis or treatment – such as failure to detect cancer when it is present.

3.22 Initiatives deployed to reduce risks to health in these examples and others like them include: information and labelling, health education, counselling and support, skills training, regulation, legislation to manage the performance of health services and good surveillance.

3.23 Perhaps because of the very diversity of factors which can pose a risk to health, perhaps because of their complexity, or perhaps because of the apparently unique circumstances of each, no clear ground rules have been established in the past on the interventions to be used when a hazard poses a risk to human health.

'a balance between risk and personal freedom'

3.24 In some fields of health, being exposed to a risk carries with it no benefits and therefore the aim has to be to eliminate or substantially reduce the risk. In most other situations a potential risk must be weighed against a potential benefit. Vaccines carry great benefits. They prevent diseases which can sometimes be deadly. Against these benefits must be balanced the rare risk of an adverse reaction to the vaccine. Similarly, medicines can relieve pain, restore lost function and, sometimes, save life. They carry risks in the form of side-effects, some minor, some major.

3.25 In short, it is the role of the Government to provide information about risk. But in most cases it is for the individual to decide whether to take the risk. And there is also a balance between risk and personal freedom. Some people enjoy pursuing outdoor sports which others would consider too dangerous to undertake. As long as people are aware of the risk which they are taking, it is their decision whether to put themselves at risk.

Guiding principles and key steps

3.26 The guiding principles and key steps in our approach to risk are:

Guiding principles

- high quality assessment of science

- full risk/benefit evaluation

- consistency of approach across risk areas

- clear framework of interventions

- approach should have integrity if judged in retrospect

- protect the vulnerable

- realistic sharing of uncertainty

- information should provide insight

- greater public participation in risk deliberations

Key steps

- ensuring that there is access to high quality scientific and medical advice

- communicating to the public an assessment of risk at an early stage making clear the areas of uncertainty

- giving advice where there is public anxiety because people do not know what sort of a risk they might be facing

- identifying the options for intervening to eliminate, reduce or control the risk

- selecting the appropriate option(s) in a way which involves the public and evaluates its appropriateness against specific criteria

- ensuring that the intervention is successful in controlling the risk for which it was intended

Healthy citizens

3.27 People can, do and should make their own decisions about their own and their families' health. But the Government can help, acting through local organisations in the community, to make sure that people have the best information available on which to base their decisions – on risk, for example, or on assessing health or health problems.

3.28 We know that people are generally well-informed about some health risks, the effect of smoking on health, for example. But there are other areas where people are not so well-informed, such as the way in which stress can cause physical ill-health.

3.29 In helping individuals to improve their own and their families' health, our new approach to better health will focus on the *Healthy Citizens* programme. This programme will have three principal strands, all aimed at ensuring people have the knowledge and expertise they need to deal with illnesses and health problems:

- *NHS Direct*
- *Health Skills*
- *Expert Patients*

'Healthy Citizens programme ensuring people have the knowledge and expertise they need'

NHS Direct

3.30 *NHS Direct* is a major new initiative aimed at empowering people in relation to health, providing rapid access to professional health advice and information. It is a nurse-led telephone helpline already covering 40 per cent of the population, to be implemented across the country by the end of the year 2000. *NHS Direct* will be a new gateway to health services, providing the public with prompt and comprehensive access to health information and advice.

3.31 *NHS Direct* provides access, 24 hours a day and 365 days a year, to comprehensive good quality information and professional advice on health, illness and the NHS with seamless links to specialist information providers on topics such as cancer, mental illness, asthma and so on.

20 Most common symptoms on which advice is sought from _NHS Direct_

Adults

abdominal pain
fever
headache
chest pain
vomiting
breathing difficulty
back pain
urinary disorder
sore throat
cough
rash
diarrhoea
cold/flu
dizziness
finger and toe injuries
toothache
joint pain
vaginal bleeding
skin wound problems
leg pain

Children

fever
vomiting
rash
diarrhoea
cough
cold/flu
abdominal pain
headache
crying baby
head injury
earache
chicken pox
poisoning - ingestion
upper respiratory infection
eczema
bone injury
ligament/muscle injury
finger and toe injuries
breathing difficulties
wounds

Source: data from _NHS Direct_ sites, April 1999

3.32 Besides taking incoming calls, _NHS Direct_ nurses can call with help and advice, for instance reminding people who may need a flu jab to make an appointment, or contacting a mother who has just left hospital with her new baby to make sure that they are all right. Pilots will start by the end of the year in the West Midlands, West Yorkshire and other parts of the country. _NHS Direct_ will also aim to provide integrated access to advice and care out of hours. Pilots will be taking place in Nottingham, West London and the North East during this year. We believe that _NHS Direct_ will benefit people wherever they live. We expect that it will be especially valuable to rural areas where people may have difficulties reaching health care by public transport. People in small communities may also particularly value the confidentiality of _NHS Direct_.

NHS Direct On-line

3.33 From autumn 1999 _NHS Direct On-line_ will start to give people access, at the click of a mouse, to an interactive self-care guide and accredited information about hundreds of diseases and self-care groups. For instance, the service will provide access to a comprehensive range of information on cancers including links to specialist information providers. The interactive self-care guide will direct users through a simple set of questions, and it will be based on the twenty top symptoms on which callers most regularly seek advice from the telephone help-line. The guide will help people decide whether it is safe to look after themselves and offer advice on what they need to do. It will also help them decide when they need professional help. Where people are still unclear what to do they will always have the option of speaking to an _NHS Direct_ nurse.

3.34 Public access points for _NHS Direct_ and _NHS Direct On-line_ will be provided in a range of public places such as surgeries, pharmacies, Accident & Emergency departments, shelters for homeless people, healthy living centres, libraries and post offices. The first 100-200 will be in place by April 2000.

NHS Direct Healthcare Guide

3.35 The experience of the telephone helpline will be used to develop an *NHS Direct* Healthcare Guide, which will provide further help to people in getting the assistance they need. This will provide advice on common ailments and problems on which *NHS Direct* nurses most commonly advise. The guide will be presented in a way which supplements the advice a nurse can give over the phone. It will be sent out to callers by *NHS Direct* nurses when they think it will be helpful and it will also be available on request and through bookshops. The guide will also be appropriate for use as a basis for general training on self-care and health skills.

Health skills

Health skills for first aid

3.36 A number of NHS bodies including many ambulance services already provide first aid training. There are also many good examples of voluntary initiatives in this area, as we acknowledged in *Developing Emergency Services in the Community* published in September 1997. For example, the Red Cross, St John Ambulance, the Resuscitation Council and the Royal Society for the Prevention of Accidents as well as the BBC's 999 Roadshow and others provide training in first aid. We will build on those initiatives by investing £1 million a year to expand training for people to learn health skills including first aid, mainly using existing providers. This should pay for 1,000–1,500 extra courses and enable around 25,000 more people each year to receive training. This additional training, covering maintenance of airways, breathing and ventilation, will be linked with the *NHS Direct* Healthcare Guide which is being developed as part of the extension of *NHS Direct*. The first new courses should be available from January next year.

'NHS Direct Healthcare Guide will provide advice on common ailments and problems'

'expand training for people to learn health skills including first aid, for 25,000 more people each year'

Health skills: defibrillators

3.37 In England only two to three people in every 100 survive a cardiac arrest compared with eight to nine in Scotland and 11 in the United States. A number of the deaths in this country are avoidable: there is good evidence that people trained in the use of defibrillators can use them effectively to save lives following cardiac arrest. While we welcome the initiatives already being undertaken by the voluntary aid societies to make such equipment more widely available in the community, there is much more which can be done, both in terms of providing life-saving equipment in places where it is needed, and in training people in its use.

3.38 So we are investing an extra £2 million in a new initiative with the voluntary aid societies to save more lives following cardiac arrest. About half that sum will be available for new equipment to supplement the extra machines already being provided by the societies. That will enable us to buy about 400 additional defibrillators.

3.39 Initially we shall pilot their use in those public places where they are most needed, for example in railway stations, airports and other public areas used by large numbers of people where the incidence of cardiac arrest is likely to be relatively high. We will ensure that the responsibility for maintaining them is clearly allocated, and for ensuring that they are clearly visible and accessible so that members of the public can use them as soon as it is clear that they are needed.

3.40 The other half of the extra £2 million will be used for the provision of a linked programme of training in the use of defibrillators. We will work with the voluntary sector and others to ensure that such training is made available to support the provision of new equipment. Our aim will be to target training primarily on those who work in or near the pilot sites but we will also provide additional training opportunities for members of the public. This will help to de-medicalise and demystify immediate care and enable more people to be both competent and confident in managing emergencies. This will complement our investment in new equipment for NHS

'In England only two to three people in every 100 survive a cardiac arrest compared to eight to nine in Scotland and 11 in the United States'

bodies, including ambulance services, which will facilitate the implementation of the *National Service Framework for Coronary Heart Disease* (see paragraph 6.16).

Health foundation skills

3.41 We will also invest in schemes aimed specifically at preventing injury in children. In Oxford we are providing funds to pilot an injury minimisation programme for schools. The aim is to educate 11-year-olds in injury prevention and resuscitation skills. If the evaluation of the scheme shows it to be effective – the results are expected later this year – we will invest in additional schemes elsewhere in the country. We will initially set aside up to £500,000 a year to enable similar schemes to be provided in each health region of the country. This will be targeted on deprived areas where the incidence of childhood accidents is highest (see paragraph 2.10). It should enable around 5,000 children each year to benefit from this training.

3.42 We will establish a *Health Skills* programme for young people, with two central aims. First, it will provide young people with new opportunities to learn and acquire skills which will help them to maintain their health as they move into adult life, including for example by resisting pressure from their peers to take risks with their health. Secondly, by teaching young people how to provide first aid, including resuscitation techniques, and how to recognise common illnesses, we will equip young people with the awareness, knowledge and skills to recognise and help another person whose life may be threatened by illness.

3.43 The *Health Skills* programme will build on the proposals put forward by the Qualifications and Curriculum Authority in its recently launched consultation document on the national curriculum. In that document the Authority proposes to strengthen the citizenship and personal, health and social education components of the national curriculum in ways which will encourage young people to adopt healthy lifestyles and become much more informed, active and responsible citizens. When children leave school, they should have the skills to cope with a wide range of emergency situations, including burns, falls, bleeding and stings.

Injury Minimisation Programme for Schools (IMPS)

The IMPS project in Oxford aims to educate 11 year-olds in injury prevention and resuscitation. In a joint venture between health and education professionals and the local community the programme links first aid training into the national curriculum.

It raises children's awareness, knowledge and skills in:

- minimising injuries
- basic life support
- reducing environmental risk factors

It has proved popular with schools and pupils and has the potential to produce a generation of children who will grow up with a different attitude to the risks and prevention of accidents. They will also be more knowledgeable about the immediate care of those around them.

ARTHRITIS CARE
Challenging Arthritis

Challenging Arthritis is a self-management programme for people with arthritis run by the voluntary organisation Arthritis Care. It involves six weekly sessions of about 2.5 hours each. All the training staff and volunteers are people with arthritis. Through its *Arthritis Self-Help Course* it helps to give people with arthritis the skills to:

- take more control of their lives

- make best use of professional advice

- use their experience of arthritis to help others as well as themselves.

Already results show that this approach brings benefits additional to those from sound medical care and that it is highly effective to use trained volunteers in this way. In particular the course has:

- improved the management of all forms of arthritis, through better understanding of symptoms and improved communication with medical staff

- significantly decreased pain, fatigue and anxiety

- significantly increased use of exercise and relaxation techniques.

3.44 We envisage the *Health Skills* programme as a distinctive strand in the joint Department of Health/Department for Education and Employment *Healthy Schools* programme (see paragraph 4.17). So it will be included in the broader context of the wider curriculum changes. We will develop effective models and partnerships to ensure the early implementation of the programme. The first step will be to test current work where it exists, pilot and evaluate new approaches and explore the feasibility of different models. This will help ensure that the programme which is introduced meets young people's needs in a relevant, timely and effective way.

Health skills for parents

3.45 We will also provide health skills training for parents of young children to help ensure that children have the best possible start in life. The *Sure Start* programme, targeted at the most disadvantaged children, provides the means for doing so. *Sure Start* aims to improve children's health as well as their social and emotional development and ability to learn. As one strand of the programme we will ensure that support and advice on health, first aid and action in emergencies is provided for parents and carers. Some of the services to be provided by the first 21 projects include:

- In Barrow-in-Furness, offering support in dealing with feeding problems and weaning advice, and providing a telephone helpline open seven days a week

- In Haringey, a *What's Where* resource pack giving details of local services for families and children in the area

- In Manchester, recruitment of a dietician and provision of nutritional advice to improve the health of young children.

Health skills for later life

3.46 We know that the winter poses serious threats to the lives of older people. The English House Condition Survey found that in this country there were 4.3 million 'fuel poor' households (where more than 10 per cent of the household's income has to be spent for adequate heating), with people aged over 60 years making up nearly half of that number. We are already taking action to address fuel poverty and improve energy efficiency; in addition we are working with older people themselves to improve the effectivness of our *Keep Warm, Keep Well* campaign.

Expert patients

3.47 The final strand of our Healthy Citizens initiative is the *Expert Patients* programme to help deal with chronic illness. As people live longer an increasing number will suffer from a chronic disease. Amongst people over 75 years, around two thirds suffer from long-standing illness or disability. One national survey found that almost a quarter of people over 75 years suffered from arthritis or rheumatism, while 4 per cent were diabetic. Even at younger ages chronic diseases are common.

3.48 We want these people to have more years of healthy, active life. We shall help people with chronic disease maintain their health, improve their quality of life and slow the progression of conditions which can lead to pain, serious incapacity and premature death.

3.49 People with chronic illnesses are often in the best position to know how to cope. There is increasing evidence from research studies and from patients' associations that people have improved health and reduced incapacity if they take the lead themselves in managing their chronic disease – with good support from the health service.

3.50 But in the past, too little has been done to help people with chronic disease to play a part in managing their own condition. That is why we have asked the Chief Medical Officer to set up a Task Force to design the new *Expert Patients* programme to address the needs of the very many people in this country with a chronic disease or disability, who amount to one in three of the total population. The Task Force will look at the role which those affected can themselves play as experts in managing their chronic disease. It will set out the relationship between such programmes and the support which people require from the NHS. It will design a pilot programme and provide advice on what needs to be done to make services for people with chronic disease a central part of the NHS. In this way we hope to improve their self-esteem and their quality of life.

ASTHMA

The National Asthma Campaign reports that doctors often do not understand the advantages which self-treatment regimes can bring. If they were more widely taken up it could provide great benefits both to people suffering from asthma and to the NHS.

This applies both to **adults,** where randomised controlled trials of self-treatment regimes have shown:

- a reduction in asthma symptoms

- a reduction in emergency visits

- a reduction in hospitalisation

- fewer days off work

and to **children**

- a recent randomised controlled trial in Glasgow showed how a 45-minute education session with a nurse could significantly reduce the number of children readmitted to hospital with asthma

- a similar programme in Leicester has shown similar results from a 20 minute session with a nurse.

Twelve ways in which people can help themselves to deal with long-standing illnesses

- recognising and acting on symptoms
- using medication correctly
- managing emergencies
- maintaining nutrition and diet
- taking adequate physical activity
- stopping smoking
- using stress reduction techniques
- effectively accessing health services
- managing psychological responses to illness
- using community resources
- adapting to work
- managing significant relationships with others

Source: derived from Lorig K L et al. Medical Care, 1999; 37 5-14.

4 Communities: tackling the wider causes of ill-health

4.1 Individual behaviour is often vitally important in improving, safeguarding or damaging health. But poor health can also spring from a complex interaction between the genetic make-up and behaviour of individuals and social, economic and environmental factors in the community.

4.2 Health is also profoundly unequal. Health inequality runs throughout life, from before birth through into old age. It exists between social classes, different areas of the country, between men and women, and between people from different ethnic backgrounds. But the story of health inequality is clear: the poorer you are, the more likely you are to be ill and to die younger. That is true for almost every health problem.

'Health inequality runs throughout life'

'run-down communities have suffered most'

4.3 Over recent years it is the health and well-being of people living in the most run-down communities which have suffered most. Poverty, low wages and occupational stress, unemployment, poor housing, environmental pollution, poor education, limited access to transport and shops, crime and disorder, and a lack of recreational facilities all have had an impact on people's health.

Health inequality

- life expectancy at birth for a boy is about five years less in the two lowest social classes than in the two highest, at 70 and 75 years respectively

- each of the main disease groups shows a wide health gap among men, with those in the highest two social classes experiencing lower mortality than men in the lowest two

- men aged between 20 and 64 from the bottom social class are three times more likely to die from coronary heart disease and stroke than those in the top social class

- mortality from all major causes has been found to be consistently higher than average among unemployed men; unemployed women have higher mortality from coronary heart disease and suicide

- children from manual households are more likely to suffer from chronic sickness than children from non-manual households

- children from manual households are more likely to suffer from tooth decay than children from non-manual households

- men in manual classes are about 40 per cent more likely to report a long-standing illness that limits their activities than those in non-manual classes.

4.4 The impact that could be made by an attack on health inequality is clear. For example, if the death rates of all men of working age were the same as those in professional and managerial jobs, about 17,000 deaths would be avoided each year of which about 75 per cent would be in our four priority areas: cancer, coronary heart disease and stroke, accidents and suicide.

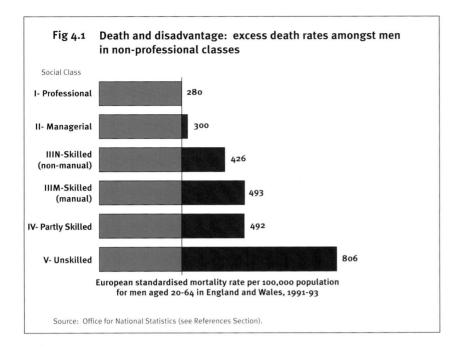

Fig 4.1   Death and disadvantage: excess death rates amongst men in non-professional classes

Social Class

I- Professional   280

II- Managerial   300

IIIN-Skilled (non-manual)   426

IIIM-Skilled (manual)   493

IV- Partly Skilled   492

V- Unskilled   806

European standardised mortality rate per 100,000 population for men aged 20-64 in England and Wales, 1991-93

Source: Office for National Statistics (see References Section).

4.5   The Acheson Inquiry, which published its Report in November 1998, confirmed that for many aspects of health, inequality has generally worsened in the last few decades, especially in the 1980s and early 1990s.

4.6   The Government is publishing an action plan on tackling health inequality at the same time as this White Paper. The plan addresses the social, economic and environmental factors and the part they play in poor health.

'The Acheson Inquiry confirmed inequality has generally worsened in the last few decades'

The scale of the challenge

4.7   Successful health education campaigns in the past have tended to widen inequality, because the better off took more notice and changed their behaviour faster than others did. We are determined to make sure that future campaigns are designed to have most effect on those most need in need (see paragraph 11.6).

'we refuse to accept such inequality as inevitable'

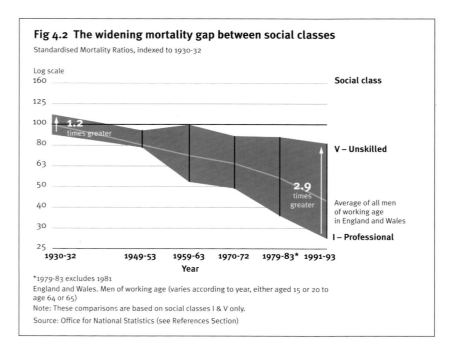

Fig 4.2 The widening mortality gap between social classes
Standardised Mortality Ratios, indexed to 1930-32

Log scale

Social class

V – Unskilled

2.9 times greater

Average of all men of working age in England and Wales

I – Professional

1.2 times greater

Year: 1930-32   1949-53   1959-63   1970-72   1979-83*   1991-93

*1979-83 excludes 1981
England and Wales. Men of working age (varies according to year, either aged 15 or 20 to age 64 or 65)
Note: These comparisons are based on social classes I & V only.
Source: Office for National Statistics (see References Section)

4.8 During the 1980s and 1990s the gap between rich and poor widened and the health gap grew wider. We are determined to close it in the new millennium. Our policies will have the cumulative effect of setting us on a new course of regenerating health on a massive scale with most effort targeted on those most in need.

Evening up opportunity

'we fully accept the responsibility of Government to address such deep-seated problems'

4.9 While the roots of health inequality run deep, we refuse to accept such inequality as inevitable. Moreover, we fully accept the responsibility of Government to address such deep-seated problems. That is why we are committed to a wide-ranging programme of action, right across Government, to tackle them.

4.10 Because tackling social exclusion is one of the Government's highest priorities the Prime Minister established a Social Exclusion Unit at the heart of Whitehall. Health is an important dimension of social exclusion, which involves not only social but also economic and psychological isolation. Although people may know what affects their health, they can find it difficult to act on what they know, setting up a downward spiral of deprivation and poor health.

4.11 In some areas there is persistent inequality between men and women. The Women's Unit which we have established in the Cabinet Office dovetails with the work of the Social Exclusion Unit. Current work on tackling violence against women, parity in old age, balancing home and work, teenage girls and risk behaviour, all have relevance for improving health and cutting inequality.

4.12 Action to tackle health inequality needs to be targeted in different ways in different places. An inner city area will need different approaches from a remote rural area. We shall publish an Urban White Paper and a Rural White Paper which will, amongst other things, address the health needs of local communities and social exclusion.

Security and health

4.13 The strong association between low income and ill-health is clear. For many people the best route out of poverty is through employment. We are making it easier for people to escape from the benefits trap into work, for example through our tax and benefit reforms, such as the Working Families Tax Credit and the Childcare Tax Credit and through introducing the first ever national minimum wage in this country.

4.14 For those who cannot work, a secure income is important to safeguard their health. We are determined to provide them with the security they need. That is why the Department of Social Security is working to ensure that people who are entitled to benefits actually claim them. Mothers with young children may find it very difficult to combine their family responsibilities with adequately paid employment. We are therefore introducing changes that will make work pay and good quality child care affordable. And we are targeting support towards all families with young children by increasing child benefit by the highest ever amount, and increasing the allowances for children in the income-related benefits.

'making it easier for people to escape from the benefits trap into work'

'introducing the first ever national minimum wage in this country'

45

4.15 Older people too and some disabled people are unlikely to be in full-time work – we have introduced a minimum income guarantee for pensioners and a disability income guarantee for the most severely disabled people. We have allocated £500 million to make winter fuel payments part of all pensioners' income. We have also given pensioners an entitlement to free NHS eye-tests. We are committed to a national minimum standard for local authority concessionary fare schemes of half-fare on buses. The Green Paper *Partnership in Pensions*, published last December, described our proposals for a *New Insurance Contract* for pensions, with a minimum income guarantee for pensioners.

Education and health

'by improving education we will tackle one of the main causes of inequality in health'

4.16 Education is vital to health. People with low levels of educational achievement are more likely to have poor health as adults. So by improving education for all we will tackle one of the main causes of inequality in health. Education can build self-esteem and can equip children and young people with the skills to adopt a healthier lifestyle. Education can also contribute to general improvement in health by enhancing people's ability to secure opportunities for work.

4.17 We set out in our White Paper *Excellence in schools* our commitment to early years education and to helping all schools to become healthy schools. A healthy school is one where good health and social behaviour underpin effective learning and academic achievement, which in turn promotes long-term health gain. The *Healthy Schools* programme has set up pilot partnerships between education and health authorities to provide the context and support for a healthy environment for school communities. Building on the lessons from the pilots we expect to roll out the scheme nationally from the autumn. The national programme, supported in 1999-2000 with £4 million jointly from the Department of Health and the Department for Education and Employment, will provide the opportunity for all schools to participate.

4.18 The programme has also set up a wide range of supporting projects to assist schools in meeting the standards expected by a national scheme. These include:

- *Wired for Health,* www.wiredforhealth.gov.uk
  a website designed specifically for schools with information to help young people make informed decisions about their health and assist teachers in dealing with health issues in schools

- *Cooking for kids,* a programme that supports the teaching of basic cooking and food preparation skills, facts about nutrition and food hygiene to children in the school holidays. By the end of the summer we expect to have involved over 15,000 children across England. The *Cooking for kids* programme is part of a long-term strategy for cutting coronary heart disease and cancer by giving children an understanding of what makes a diet healthy. It provides opportunities for expanding the provision of school breakfast clubs and improving the nutritional value of school meals

'the Cooking for kids programme is a long term strategy for cutting heart disease and cancer'

- The *Safer Travel to School* scheme, supporting schools in devising projects that will encourage children to walk or cycle to school along safe routes, with a view to promoting exercise and changing the reliance on the car for the 'school run', reducing congestion on the roads and promoting a safer and cleaner environment.

'a step change in school sport'

4.19 We recognise the vital contribution that physical activity makes as one of the foundation subjects of the national curriculum. Good physical education and school sports provision are essential to the foundation of lifelong positive attitudes towards health and fitness. We support the work that Sport England does to put in place a sound framework for physical education and sport through its *Active Schools* programme. Ensuring a step change in the provision of school sport will be a major message of the Government's *Sports Strategy* paper.

Employment and health

Men unemployed at both 1971 and 1981 Censuses had mortality double that of all men in the same age range; men unemployed at only one Census had an excess mortality of 27 per cent.

'the opportunity to move off benefit and into work'

Employment and health

4.20 People in work enjoy better physical and mental health than those without work. Unemployment increases the risk of illness and premature death. For example: a middle-aged man who loses his job is twice as likely to die in the next five years as a man who remains employed.

4.21 Under the *New Deal*, young people, the long-term unemployed, lone parents and disabled people are being offered the opportunity to move off benefit and into work. We are investing £3.9 billion in the period to 2001-2 in *Welfare to Work* programmes which will help equip people with the education and skills they need to get jobs and keep them.

4.22 But people can also be exposed in the workplace to health risks. Minimum standards for health and safety at work are laid down in legislation. But levels of work-related ill-health are still high. In 1995 in Great Britain two million people suffered from a work-related illness, and around 20 million working days were lost through work-related ill-health – though this is partly due to wider economic and industrial changes which affect patterns of work-related ill-health.

Numbers of days lost from work-related illness[1]

Musculoskeletal (including back pain)	11 million
Stress, depression or anxiety	5 million
Trauma	1 million
Other	4 million

Source: Self-Reported Work-Related Illness 1995, HSE, p.52

1 Days lost sum to be more than 20 million because individuals who take time off due to more than one type of illness are counted in each illness category.

4.23 Last summer the Health and Safety Executive launched a discussion document to develop a new occupational health strategy. In addition, the Deputy Prime Minister has announced a strategic appraisal of health and safety, to inject a new impetus into the health and safety agenda 25 years after the Health and Safety at Work etc Act 1974. A consultation document will be launched in July and the outcome of the appraisal will be announced in November.

4.24 Effective action by employers and employees will improve competitiveness by reducing sickness absence rates; it will also improve the health of the local communities which provide the workforce.

4.25 The workplace provides opportunities both to improve the health of the workforce and to address health inequality. The health of people at work is a core issue for management. A healthy workforce is a pre-condition for competitiveness and business success.

4.26 Some work conditions can have a profound impact on health. For example, the evidence shows that people in jobs which place high demands on them over which they have no control are at much higher risk of coronary heart disease – one of our four priority areas. A healthy workplace will bring employers and employees improved productivity, lower rates of sickness absence, fewer accidents and less illness.

4.27 In March 1999 the Ministers for Public Health and for Health and Safety launched the *Healthy Workplace* Initiative, based on the message that *Improving Health is Everybody's Business*. The initiative will promote healthy workplaces by:

- developing examples of good practice for handling key workplace health issues

- making available relevant and up-to-date information, for example to help alleviate back pain

- encouraging better access to services and helping to provide a bridge between prevention, treatment and rehabilitation

- helping to promote compliance with relevant workplace legislation

'Effective action will improve competitiveness by reducing sickness absence'

Housing and health

'good quality housing inevitably has an important impact on health'

4.28 Most people spend more time in their own homes than anywhere else. So good quality housing inevitably has an important impact on health. Homes should be safe, warm, dry and well-ventilated with amenities which meet minimum standards of comfort, such as indoor toilets. There are still about 1.5 million dwellings which fall short of the current housing fitness standard laid down in primary legislation.

4.29 The most important risks to health from poor housing come from cold and damp, which cause a number of illnesses including respiratory diseases. Very old people, small children and the chronically sick are most vulnerable to this increased risk. Typically, in any one winter there will be 2.5 million homes in England cold enough to cause ill-health, and two million of those will be occupied by people in these vulnerable groups. From December to March, year on year, there are between 20,000 and 50,000 excess deaths compared to the rest of the year. Cold housing is one of the factors responsible. *Keep Warm Keep Well* for older people is one of the ways we shall tackle this issue (see paragraph 3.46).

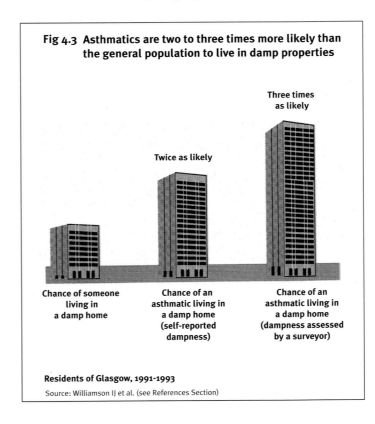

Fig 4.3 Asthmatics are two to three times more likely than the general population to live in damp properties

Three times as likely

Twice as likely

Chance of someone living in a damp home

Chance of an asthmatic living in a damp home (self-reported dampness)

Chance of an asthmatic living in a damp home (dampness assessed by a surveyor)

Residents of Glasgow, 1991-1993

Source: Williamson IJ et al. (see References Section)

4.30 We are reviewing the current fitness standard and have proposed replacing it with a new rating system which is currently being piloted. This would include all the important health and safety risks in the home including poor energy efficiency. The new system would provide a more effective way of identifying those dwellings which present the worst risks and taking action to remedy them. A *National Licensing System* for houses in multiple occupation will help tackle the worst housing conditions.

4.31 Many people live in homes which do not use energy efficiently. This pushes up the cost of household fuel bills. Those people are likely to be the most vulnerable members of society – those with low incomes, families with young children and older people. We have reviewed our entire fuel poverty policy to see how we can bring extra help to these vulnerable people. We are now consulting on our proposals.

'fuel poverty policy to help vulnerable people'

Housing and health

- The *Housing Investment Programme* and the *Capital Receipts Initiative* have already provided an extra £800 million in 1997/8 and 1998/9, benefiting 300,000 existing homes and supporting the provision of 4,000 extra new homes for people in housing need; together they are providing a total of £5.3 billion over the next three years to address poor housing, enabling local authorities to improve 1.5 million council homes.

- The *Housing Corporation Approved Development Programme*, which funds investment by registered local landlords, will total £2.6 billion over the next three years.

- *Private Sector Housing Disabled Facilities Grants* are targeting assistance where there is the greatest need, with grants for renovation and home repair for less well-off owners; special grants for disabled people to adapt their homes for independent living; a total of £212 million for disabled facilities over the next three years.

- We are giving Home Improvement Agencies an additional £4.2 million, bringing the total to £19.8 million over the next three years, to extend the advice and help they give to the most vulnerable with repairs, improvements and insulation.

- *The New Home Energy Efficiency Scheme* will help some 500,000 households move substantially out of fuel poverty during 2000–2002. Including the schemes in Scotland and Wales, there will be a total of £300 million available in these first two years.

'to reduce the number of people sleeping rough by two thirds by 2002'

Homelessness

4.32 Homelessness is one of the worst effects of social exclusion and can be a significant cause of ill-health. We have pledged to place a new duty on local authorities to protect those who are homeless through no fault of their own and who are in priority need. We have already strengthened the safety net for homeless people and ensured that households which are accepted as unintentionally homeless and in priority need are given reasonable preference in the allocation of permanent social housing. We are also considering what more help they may need.

4.33 Our aim is to reduce the number of people sleeping rough by two thirds by 2002. Following the recommendations of the Social Exclusion Unit in July 1998, we announced that a new London Rough Sleepers Unit with a budget of £145 million over three years would co-ordinate Government initiatives in the capital. The Unit has started to tackle the full range of housing, health care, education and training needs of people sleeping rough in London. The Government has also announced a new £34 million *Homelessness Action Programme* to tackle rough sleeping and single homelessness outside London. This programme helps to support local strategies addressing rough sleeping and single homelessness.

Healthy neighbourhoods

4.34 People relate closely to their neighbourhoods, and are likely to be healthier when they live in neighbourhoods where there is a sense of pride and belonging. Evidence, particularly from the World Health Organisation, shows how social cohesion and strong social networks benefit health.

4.35 The Neighbourhood Renewal Policy Action Team set up by the Social Exclusion Unit and headed by the Department for Culture, Media and Sport has found that participation in arts and sport can promote social cohesion by building strong social networks. Health action zones, healthy living centres and family doctor practices all offer the potential to promote active lifestyles to benefit local communities.

4.36 The close link between regeneration and health is reflected in our *New Deal for Communities* initiative – a key part of our work to turn around our most deprived neighbourhoods. Under it we have set up a new fund, worth £800 million over three years, to help improve the poorest neighbourhoods and encourage local people and agencies – public, private and voluntary – to work together to overcome the problems of multiple deprivation and to make a lasting improvement to their neighbourhoods.

4.37 At the same time we are targeting a reshaped Single Regeneration Budget (SRB) – worth £2.4 billion over three years – on the most deprived local authority areas and creating 50 large comprehensive schemes – at least one in each of those areas by the end of this Parliament. SRB schemes can contribute to improvements in health by developing partnerships with local health bodies to counter factors which make neighbourhoods unhealthy and to promote healthier lifestyles and improve access to community-based health facilities.

4.38 *Health For All* and *Local Agenda 21* are both long-standing local authority commitments which bring together improvements in health with improving the environment. The World Health Organisation's *Healthy Cities Programme* is one strand of *Health For All*, promoting an integrated approach to improving people's physical, social, mental and environmental well-being through putting health on the agenda for the decision-makers in cities and building a strong lobby for public health at local level.

4.39 Under *Local Agenda 21*, a comprehensive action plan at the local level to promote sustainable development for the 21st Century in urban and rural areas alike, many communities have focused on action which also delivers improvements to health. Projects such as establishing allotments and community gardens engage inner city communities in improving the local environment and producing fresh fruit and vegetables, leading to employment, improved diet and a stronger sense of community.

4.40 Underpinning all these initiatives is our planning policy which has at its heart the need for sustainable communities. Health is an important aspect of sustainability, as we recognised in our recently published good practice statement *Sustainable*

'£800 million over three years, to help improve the poorest neighbourhoods'

'a reshaped Single Regeneration Budget worth £2.4 billion over three years'

Development: Towards Better Practice. We shall continue to use the planning system to support local shopping facilities which are accessible to non-car users, to encourage healthier transport options such as walking and cycling, to promote more sustainable patterns of development for housing, and to prevent the loss of playing fields which form an essential resource for promoting the enjoyment of physical recreation.

Environment and health

4.41 People value, enjoy and draw benefit from a good and healthy environment. The link between health and the environment is long-established. We now have a better understanding of the diverse ways in which the environment can affect health - the factors which cause pollution, for example, and the way in which they affect health.

4.42 We are addressing these issues:

Environment and health

100,000 houses in the UK have high levels of radon gas – radon exposure is associated with an increased risk of certain cancers

The environment and health

- the *National Air Quality Strategy* was reviewed in 1998 with the aim of strengthening the level of health protection by setting tough targets over the next few years

- the White Paper *New Deal For Transport* recognises the link between transport and health by setting out proposals for improving public transport; encouraging walking and cycling; and by reducing emissions and pollutants from vehicles

- *A Better Quality of Life – a strategy for sustainable development in the UK* was issued in May 1999. It sets out four main aims:

  - social progress which recognises the needs of everyone

  - effective protection of the environment

  - prudent use of natural resources

  - maintenance of high and stable levels of economic growth.

4.43 Poor air quality is a serious health hazard. In 1998 the Committee on the Medical Effects of Air Pollutants published a telling report on the problem – *Quantification of the Effects of Air Pollution on Health in the United Kingdom*. Air pollution is thought to be responsible for shortening as many as 24,000 lives each year. Particulates in the air are likely to be responsible for bringing forward the deaths of 8,100 people in the UK every year, and to contribute to an additional 10,500 hospital admissions for respiratory problems. Our tough health-based targets for improving air quality will lead to substantial improvements over the next few years, including a reduction in the amount of ill-health due to poor air quality.

4.44 The UK Government hosted the largest ever Ministerial conference on environment and health in June 1999, leading the way in Europe on joined-up approaches to the wider determinants of health. Ministers from over 50 countries agreed action in partnership on many important factors impacting on health – water, transport, climate change, the workplace – looking forward to healthier nations in the 21st Century.

'health-based targets for improving air quality'

Health Impact Assessment

4.45 We need to ensure that in all areas of Government policy-making the actions that flow from our policies will contribute to our goals of improving the health of the population and reducing inequality. So we have decided that major new Government policies should be assessed for their impact on health.

4.46 This assessment process is important because it acknowledges for the first time the relationship between health and the impact of Government policy generally. We intend to make health impact assessment a part of the routine practice of policy-making in Government. We have already commissioned the first assessments of some of our major national policies, on fuel poverty and the *New Deal* for 18-24 year-olds, and we shall continue to apply the approach in other areas, right across Government.

'major new Government policies should be assessed for their impact on health'

4.47 Local decision-makers must think about the effect which their policies may have on health and in particular how they can reduce health inequality. In most cases this will require a change in the way that health authorities, local authorities and other local agencies see their role. They will in future need to act much more as health champions at local level and ensure that health is on the agenda of all local organisations and agencies outside the health field. An important part of this role will be to encourage all local agencies to make local health impact assessments when planning investment in, for example, amenities, buildings or local communities and in the location of services.

5 Saving lives: cancer

Target: to reduce the death rate from cancer in people under 75 years by at least a fifth by 2010 – saving up to 100,000 lives in total

5.1 Cancer is a word that produces a feeling of dread – a disease which can attack most parts of the body and then spread to others, and a disease which can, by returning, sometimes after long intervals, cast its shadow over the future.

5.2 In reality cancer is many different diseases affecting different organs and tissues of the body. Some types of cancer are almost completely preventable but they are not all being prevented. Some types of cancer if caught early can be cured, yet not all are being cured. Some people can be helped to survive for much longer with serious forms of cancer but many are not surviving as long as they could. Ensuring that cancer is tackled as never before is one of the biggest challenges facing us.

'cancer is one of the biggest challenges facing us'

5.3 Cancer in our country is amongst the three leading causes of death at all ages except for pre-school age children. The most common killers are lung, breast, colorectal and prostate cancer which together account for about 62,000 deaths each year.

Lung cancer

- about one fifth of all cancer cases and one quarter of cancer deaths in men are due to lung cancer

- this represents about 23,000 cases and 18,000 deaths in men each year (12,000 and 10,000 respectively in women)

- in both men and women only about six patients in every hundred will still be alive five years after diagnosis

- more than £130 million is spent by the NHS on lung cancer care each year

Breast cancer

- nearly one third of cancer cases and one fifth of cancer deaths in women are due to breast cancer

- this represents about 30,000 cases and 11,000 deaths each year

- about two thirds of women with breast cancer survive for at least five years after diagnosis

- more than £150 million is spent by the NHS on breast cancer each year

Prostate cancer

- in men approximately one cancer case in seven and one cancer death in eight are due to prostate cancer

- this represents about 15,000 cases and 8,000 deaths each year

- about two fifths of men with prostate cancer can expect to live for at least five years after diagnosis

- nearly £100 million is spent by the NHS on prostate cancer each year

Colorectal cancer

- approximately one case in seven and one death in nine from cancer in both men and women is due to colorectal cancer

- overall this represents about 28,000 cases and 14,000 deaths each year

- about two fifths of patients with colorectal cancer will live for at least five years after diagnosis

- nearly £250 million is spent by the NHS on colorectal cancer each year

5.4 Overall the risk of developing cancer appears to be increasing and there are now approximately 200,000 new cases each year. On the other hand the rate of death in the population from cancer has been falling for the last decade, though there have been strikingly different trends in death rates for individual cancers in different groups.

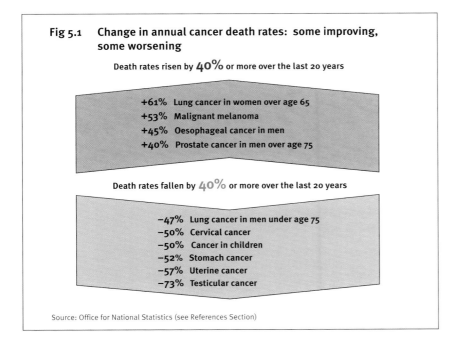

Fig 5.1 **Change in annual cancer death rates: some improving, some worsening**

Death rates risen by **40%** or more over the last 20 years

+61% Lung cancer in women over age 65
+53% Malignant melanoma
+45% Oesophageal cancer in men
+40% Prostate cancer in men over age 75

Death rates fallen by **40%** or more over the last 20 years

−47% Lung cancer in men under age 75
−50% Cervical cancer
−50% Cancer in children
−52% Stomach cancer
−57% Uterine cancer
−73% Testicular cancer

Source: Office for National Statistics (see References Section)

'Cancer attacks the population unevenly'

5.5 Explanations for these death rate trends differ. In the case of lung cancer, for example, death rates differ by gender, reflecting the fact that men took up smoking sooner than women and have also reduced their smoking rates at an earlier stage. Other cancer death rates in the population have fallen because treatment has become more effective: for example, in testicular cancer where death rates have reduced by nearly 75 per cent in the last twenty years even though the rate of new cases has grown substantially.

5.6 Cancer also attacks the population unevenly. For example, among working age men unskilled workers are twice as likely to die from cancer as professionals. There is inequality between one part of the country and another. For example women in the North West of England have a 33 per cent greater chance of suffering from cervical cancer than the national average. There is inequality between people of different ethnic origins, where for example women born in the Caribbean are about 25 per cent less likely to die from breast cancer than other women living in this country. And there is inequality between the sexes, with women more likely than men to contract melanoma skin cancer but men more likely to die from it.

How do we compare?

5.7 Overall death rates from cancer in England for people under the age of 65 years are slightly better than the average for all European Union countries. But that conceals an important difference between genders: while death rates among men are better than average, women have substantially worse than average rates especially for breast and cervical cancers.

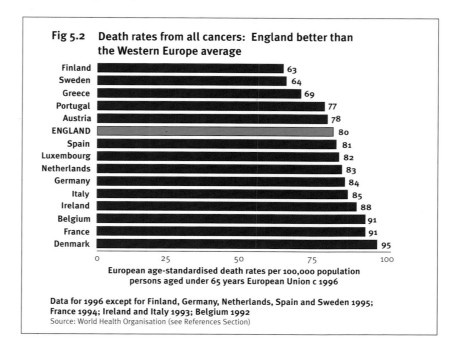

Fig 5.2 Death rates from all cancers: England better than the Western Europe average

Country	Rate
Finland	63
Sweden	64
Greece	69
Portugal	77
Austria	78
ENGLAND	80
Spain	81
Luxembourg	82
Netherlands	83
Germany	84
Italy	85
Ireland	88
Belgium	91
France	91
Denmark	95

European age-standardised death rates per 100,000 population persons aged under 65 years European Union c 1996

Data for 1996 except for Finland, Germany, Netherlands, Spain and Sweden 1995; France 1994; Ireland and Italy 1993; Belgium 1992
Source: World Health Organisation (see References Section)

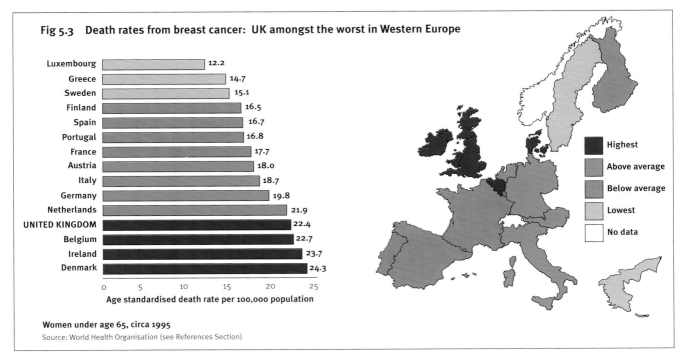

Fig 5.3 Death rates from breast cancer: UK amongst the worst in Western Europe

Country	Rate
Luxembourg	12.2
Greece	14.7
Sweden	15.1
Finland	16.5
Spain	16.7
Portugal	16.8
France	17.7
Austria	18.0
Italy	18.7
Germany	19.8
Netherlands	21.9
UNITED KINGDOM	22.4
Belgium	22.7
Ireland	23.7
Denmark	24.3

Age standardised death rate per 100,000 population

Highest
Above average
Below average
Lowest
No data

Women under age 65, circa 1995

Source: World Health Organisation (see References Section)

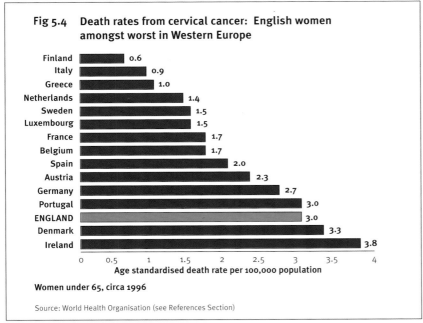

Fig 5.4 Death rates from cervical cancer: English women amongst worst in Western Europe

Country	Rate
Finland	0.6
Italy	0.9
Greece	1.0
Netherlands	1.4
Sweden	1.5
Luxembourg	1.5
France	1.7
Belgium	1.7
Spain	2.0
Austria	2.3
Germany	2.7
Portugal	3.0
ENGLAND	3.0
Denmark	3.3
Ireland	3.8

Age standardised death rate per 100,000 population

Women under 65, circa 1996

Source: World Health Organisation (see References Section)

5.8 Mortality rates in our country may be high for some cancers even though these cancers may not occur more commonly in this country. This suggests that the chances of surviving after diagnosis may be poorer here than in some other countries. For many of the main causes of cancer death – for example, lung, colorectal and breast – survival in England and Wales is lower than in the United States and lower than the average for the European Union.

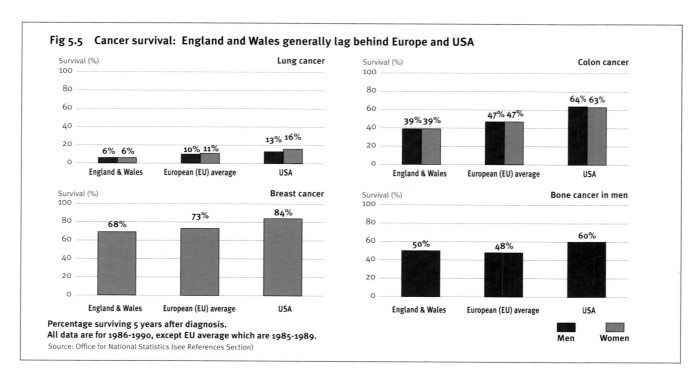

Fig 5.5   Cancer survival: England and Wales generally lag behind Europe and USA

Lung cancer — Survival (%)
- England & Wales: Men 6%, Women 6%
- European (EU) average: Men 10%, Women 11%
- USA: Men 13%, Women 16%

Colon cancer — Survival (%)
- England & Wales: Men 39%, Women 39%
- European (EU) average: Men 47%, Women 47%
- USA: Men 64%, Women 63%

Breast cancer — Survival (%)
- England & Wales: 68%
- European (EU) average: 73%
- USA: 84%

Bone cancer in men — Survival (%)
- England & Wales: 50%
- European (EU) average: 48%
- USA: 60%

Percentage surviving 5 years after diagnosis.
All data are for 1986-1990, except EU average which are 1985-1989.
Source: Office for National Statistics (see References Section)

Men   Women

5.9 There is no single explanation for these figures but part of the difference may reflect the fact that there are cancer services in other countries which are better than we are in this country at treating cancer. Even in England and Wales people in more deprived areas tend to have lower survival rates, in part reflecting the fact that they may find it harder to gain access to the services available. If all patients shared the survival rates of the best off, there would have been more than 12,700 fewer cancer deaths in England and Wales among those diagnosed between 1986 and 1990.

'people in more deprived areas tend to have lower survival rates'

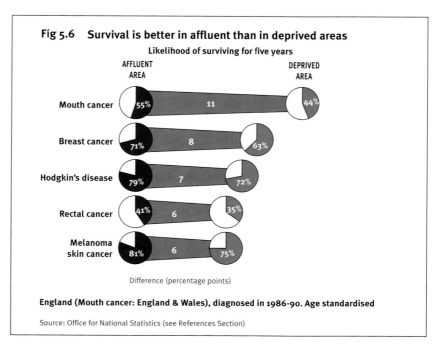

Fig 5.6   Survival is better in affluent than in deprived areas

Likelihood of surviving for five years

AFFLUENT AREA — DEPRIVED AREA

- Mouth cancer: 55% — 11 — 44%
- Breast cancer: 71% — 8 — 63%
- Hodgkin's disease: 79% — 7 — 72%
- Rectal cancer: 41% — 6 — 35%
- Melanoma skin cancer: 81% — 6 — 75%

Difference (percentage points)

England (Mouth cancer: England & Wales), diagnosed in 1986-90. Age standardised

Source: Office for National Statistics (see References Section)

Causes

5.10 Cancer occurs when the normal process of cell growth in the body goes wrong. Why this happens is not fully understood, but the causes are known to be complex. The trigger to start the process off is different for different cancers and different people. Sometimes factors which we cannot control, such as our genes, have a big part to play. Research has shown that there are several major risk factors:

- Tobacco smoking causes most lung cancer. It is also implicated in many other types of cancer. Overall about a third of all cancer deaths are caused by smoking.

- Diet accounts for about a quarter of cancer deaths in this country (as compared to about a third in developed countries as a whole). Low levels of consumption of fruit and vegetables are linked with an increased risk of colorectal and stomach cancer, and possibly some other cancers. In some cases heavy alcohol consumption is associated with a 3- to 15-fold extra risk. Those who also smoke are at even higher risk of several of these cancers.

- Exposure to infections appears to cause some cancers, and understanding of this cause is growing all the time. For instance, the hepatitis B and C viruses are associated with an increased risk of liver cancer; and the human papilloma virus, linked to most cervical cancer, which is associated with about 3,000 cases and more than 1,000 deaths from cancer each year. Hepatitis B may be transferred from mother to child at birth, and both hepatitis B and the human papilloma virus may be sexually transmitted and then infect, respectively, the liver or the cells which line the cervix. In addition stomach cancer which accounts for about 10,000 cases and 6,000 deaths each year may in many cases be associated with certain bacterial infections, particularly amongst those who grow up in disadvantaged areas.

'a third of all cancer deaths are caused by smoking'

'Pollutants in the environment may cause cancer'

- Exposure to chemicals can induce cancer. For instance asbestos fibres may lodge in the chest and may silently promote the development of several forms of cancer as well as other diseases. Approximately 3,000 deaths each year are thought to be caused in this way by asbestos exposure in Great Britain. Similarly dyes used in certain industries may increase the risk of bladder cancer

- Pollutants in the environment may cause cancer if inhaled or swallowed. So may radiation, whether through exposure to radon gas in certain homes or excessive sunlight. Getting sunburnt in childhood may result in an increased risk of skin cancer which accounts for nearly 2,000 deaths each year.

Action: reducing risk and staying healthy

5.11 By taking effective action to promote healthier behaviour and reduce exposure to risk we can make a huge impact on cancer. Two changes above all would have the greatest impact: a reduction of tobacco smoking and adoption of a diet rich in cereals and fruit and vegetables. These two steps alone could account for about a ten per cent reduction in cancer death rates in those under 75 years by 2010. Other measures too will promote health and protect people from cancer. For example, by avoiding excessive exposure to sunlight people can reduce their risk of skin cancer. In particular we must ensure that young children are not exposed to too much sun.

5.12 Our programme of health measures will contribute towards combating cancer:

- the White Paper *Smoking Kills,* published in December 1998, commits us to a new public education campaign, a network of smoking cessation clinics and the promotion of nicotine replacement therapy as well as a range of other detailed measures

- the regulations we introduced on 17 June set out our intention to ban tobacco advertising from 10 December 1999

- through our *Healthy Schools* programme, healthy living centres and elsewhere, the promotion of information on healthy diets, including cooking skills; and more effective advice for people on maintaining appropriate body weight.

5.13 Vaccines to prevent cancer already exist and are in use. For example we are running a programme to provide hepatitis B vaccine for those at increased risk of acquiring the infection. Looking to the future, more cancer vaccines are in prospect, for instance against cervical cancer in women. As we better understand the role of infections in malignant disease so, looking ten years or so into the future, we may be able to develop vaccines for their prevention. Also, in the longer term, we should be able to tailor treatments to the genetic characteristics of tumours.

Action: early recognition

5.14 Pre-symptomatic tests through screening can detect cancer either in its very first stages or, as with cervical screening, even before the disease develops. The NHS has been providing screening programmes for breast and cervical cancer since the late 1980s and in general they have been a considerable success. The cervical screening programme alone prevents up to 3,900 cases of cancer each year in the UK.

5.15 Regular screening of women aged between 50-64 years for breast cancer will eventually save up to an estimated 1,250 lives each year in the UK. And we are currently undertaking pilot studies to assess the feasibility of routinely inviting women aged 65-69 years for breast screening. These pilots are due to be completed in 2000.

5.16 However, screening does not provide a guarantee that cancerous or pre-cancerous cells will be found if they are present. And, although they have proved to be effective, screening programmes have not been as reliable as they should have been. We have taken far-reaching action to improve the quality of the service. We are reviewing the possibility of using automated techniques in the cervical screening programme. In addition we are working to ensure that women at risk of cancer take up screening invitations as we know that some groups, such as Bangladeshi women, have been reluctant to come forward. We will publish our strategy on breast and cervical screening later this year.

National Cervical Cancer Screening Programme

- the number of women dying of cervical cancer has fallen by 25 per cent since 1992

- since 1988 screening has reduced mortality by 60 per cent in those aged under 55 years

- the estimated number of lives saved in 1997 was 1,300

Source: Sasieni P and Adams J 1999 318: 1244 – 1245

5.17 So we are taking action to:

- Stop cervical screening in those laboratories which screen fewer than the recommended 15,000 smears a year and do not achieve expected results

- Require all laboratories undertaking cervical screening to apply for external accreditation

- Ensure that all health authorities should achieve 80 per cent coverage rates for cervical screening by March 2002

- Make clear that all health authorities must achieve three-yearly intervals for breast screening by March 2000.

5.18 However just because a simple and reliable test exists it does not follow that it should be offered to all healthy people to see whether they have the early stages of cancer. Early detection in itself does not prolong survival: but if a safe and effective treatment is available which can be started before symptoms would otherwise have appeared then screening can lead to a better chance of cure or improved life expectancy.

5.19 To give expert, evidence-based advice on which screening programmes should be introduced, a National Screening Committee was established. In addition to the breast and cervical cancer screening programmes which are now population-wide, pilot studies are currently being undertaken to assess the feasibility of screening for colorectal cancer. The results will be available in the year 2002. The National Screening Committee has advised that on present evidence population screening for prostate cancer would not be justified. This is being kept under review.

5.20 Besides this, our *Healthy Citizens* initiative will help. *NHS Direct* will provide an immediate advice line for people worried that they might have cancer, while our *Expert Patients* programme will help to ensure that people with the disease are best able to manage it, giving the best hope of a good outcome.

National cancer screening programmes

- Breast cancer

- Cervical cancer

- Colorectal cancer programmes – two pilots

- Research priorities – prostate; ovarian; and further research on existing and pilot programmes

Action: more effective treatment

5.21 In the middle of this century the chances of surviving cancer were low and showed little improvement from one year to the next. Over the last few decades, however, there have been some striking changes. In one form of childhood cancer – acute lymphoblastic leukaemia – the chances of surviving for at least five years were less than ten per cent over 30 years ago. By the late 1980s/early 1990s they had improved to over 70 per cent.

5.22 Between the 1960s and the 1970s survival from Hodgkin's disease nearly doubled from 30 per cent to about 55 per cent. Similarly between the 1970s and the late 1980s/early 1990s survival improved from nearly 50 per cent to more than 70 per cent for melanoma skin cancer in men and from nearly 30 per cent to nearly 40 per cent for cancer of the large bowel in women.

5.23 For other forms of cancer there has been less progress. Cancer of the prostate and of the lung, for example, have shown almost no improvement in recent years.

5.24 Effectively tackling the problem of cancer means achieving consistently high quality, specialist services for patients, with their carers and families, available to everyone. It also means providing special support, for example, to black and ethnic minorities to encourage their participation in managing their condition.

5.25 On 20 May 1999 the Prime Minister hosted a summit meeting on cancer which brought together the country's top cancer experts – patient representatives, policy-makers and health professionals – to take stock of prevention and treatment services in this country, and to define the new challenges which must be met in those services in the future.

5.26 It was recognised that there were many excellent aspects of cancer services in Britain but that overall there was much that needed to be improved if patients in all parts of the country were to benefit from the high quality of care which could be achieved in the best centres.

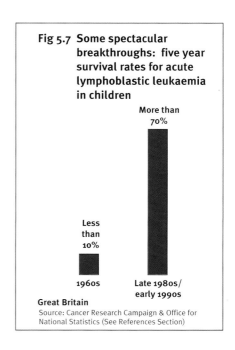

Fig 5.7 **Some spectacular breakthroughs: five year survival rates for acute lymphoblastic leukaemia in children**

More than 70%

Less than 10%

1960s   Late 1980s/ early 1990s

Great Britain
Source: Cancer Research Campaign & Office for National Statistics (See References Section)

'tackling cancer means high quality, specialist services for everyone'

5.27 As a result of that meeting a five-point action plan was published to focus attention on the essential changes that were required:

- undertake a major review of the organisation and co-ordination of cancer research in this country

- appoint a new Cancer Action Team to work with the NHS to raise the standard of cancer care in all hospitals to the level which is already being achieved by the best

- extend the series of guidance documents which set out best practice in the care of individual types of cancer. Guidance on gynaecological cancers is being published in July and on stomach cancers towards the end of the year; further documents will be published in the year 2000

- ask the Commission for Health Improvement to review cancer services across the country as an early priority

- undertake the first ever national survey of cancer patients' experiences later this year.

Integrated action

5.28 In our fight against cancer we can be successful only if everyone recognises that:

- a fundamental attack is needed on the risk factors which cause cancer, concentrating mainly on sustained reductions in smoking and improvements in diet, in which action at all levels – individual, local, Government – is co-ordinated to secure the maximum benefit

- efforts to combat the fragmentation and the variable quality of cancer treatment services, which have accounted for our past record of unequal survival patterns, must be stepped up through the five-point action plan outlined above, in order to give everyone the best chance of beating the disease

- a new strategic approach must be taken to research which recognises the links between cancer prevention and treatment, and which ensures that the practice of cancer care does not lag behind the science of cancer as it so often has in the past

- partnerships with cancer charities and other non-Governmental organisations involved in cancer treatment and research are a cornerstone of a high-quality approach to combating cancer.

'develop and implement consistent national standards'

5.29 We will develop and implement consistent national standards and develop the workforce strategy necessary to deliver high quality care. We will work with a range of organisations to look at how better to plan and share research; to provide the support and information necessary to enable individuals to participate fully in prevention and treatment decisions, and to set us on course to reduce the death rate from cancer and reduce by about 100,000 the premature deaths from this disease by 2010.

5.30 We recognise that these improvements will mean extra effort. Some of the changes we want to see will not cost money. Better communication, better organisation and changes in the way people tackle problems can be achieved without significant extra resource. But there are some areas where we need to invest for success. As well as the extra money which we are putting into cancer through the Modernisation Fund, the New Opportunities Fund is also contributing £150 million over three years across the United Kingdom to help with cancer prevention, early detection, diagnosis and treatment, and palliative care. This will build on local fundraising to meet local need. It will help in the move to fair access to high quality services across the country, and will bring together the NHS, the voluntary sector, local authorities and other local partners.

5.31 A Cancer Action Team will drive progress to achieve this target, supported by investment from the *Public Health Development Fund* (see paragraphs 11.39 and 11.40).

Fig 5.8 Ways of beating cancer: examples of how everyone can play their part

Individuals can...	Local partnerships can...	National Government will...
Give up smoking	Facilitate access to fruit and vegetables (e.g. through provision of community transport)	Increase tax on cigarettes and ban advertising
Support others (e.g. in giving up smoking)	Support local co-ops	Promote availability of cheaper fruit and vegetables
Protect others from second-hand smoke	Reduce exposure to radon in homes	Enforce regulations on exposure to asbestos and encourage provision of non-smoking areas
Protect children and themselves from sunburn	Provide smoking cessation clinics, non-smoking areas and smoke extractors	Provide health information through *NHS Direct*.
Eat more fruit and vegetables each day	Develop healthy workplaces and schools	Fund health education campaigns
Drink sensibly and practise safer sex	Provide clear information about early detection and encourage people to take up screening	Introduce an *Expert Patients* programme for people with chronic disease
Take up screening invitations		Enforce screening standards
Participate in their own self management		Ensure implementation of expert report on organisation of cancer services
		Ensure all patients with suspected cancer seen by a specialist within two weeks of GP referral, (by April 1999 for breast cancer and by 2000 for other cancers).

Contribution to target reduction in deaths from cancer by 2010 saving up to

100,000
lives in total

20%

Cut in death rate from cancer in people aged under 75 years between 1997 and 2010

6 Saving lives: coronary heart disease and stroke

Target: to reduce the death rate from coronary heart disease and stroke and related diseases in people under 75 years by at least two fifths by 2010 – saving up to 200,000 lives in total

6.1 One group of diseases kills more commonly than any other, can strike within minutes and singles out people in their prime as well as in later life. Coronary heart disease and stroke, along with other diseases of the circulatory system[1], account for over 200,000 of the half a million deaths which occur in this country each year. And while death rates are improving substantially for the best off in society, the worst off have not benefited to anything like the same extent, thus widening the health gap. Many families in our country have experienced the tragedy that these diseases can bring.

[1] In this White Paper all references to coronary heart disease and stroke should be understood to cover all diseases of the circulatory system

6.2 Many more people who survive acute heart attacks and strokes suffer long-term pain and disability. They and their families know how difficult it is to cope with these consequences. Never feeling completely well, unable to work, often confined to the house, constantly reliant on others – these are some of the worst features which many people must endure.

How do we compare?

6.3 Death rates for coronary heart disease and stroke fell during the 1970s and 1980s in most western countries and England was no exception. Deaths from coronary heart disease dropped by 38 per cent between the early 1970s and late 1990s and from stroke by 54 per cent over the same period. But across the European Union (EU), England has one of the worst rates of coronary heart disease – for people aged under 65 years, we are two and a half times worse than France (the country with the lowest rate in the EU) amongst men and over four times worse for women. For stroke, at least in those aged under 65 years, the picture is rather better with our death rates in men being better than for many other EU countries, but for women our rate is closer to the average and is more than 50 per cent higher than France, the best-performing EU country.

'England has one of the worst rates of coronary heart disease'

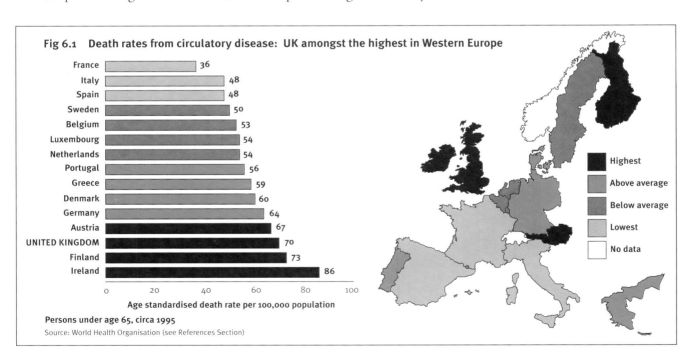

Fig 6.1   Death rates from circulatory disease: UK amongst the highest in Western Europe

Country	Rate
France	36
Italy	48
Spain	48
Sweden	50
Belgium	53
Luxembourg	54
Netherlands	54
Portugal	56
Greece	59
Denmark	60
Germany	64
Austria	67
UNITED KINGDOM	70
Finland	73
Ireland	86

Age standardised death rate per 100,000 population

Highest
Above average
Below average
Lowest
No data

Persons under age 65, circa 1995

Source: World Health Organisation (see References Section)

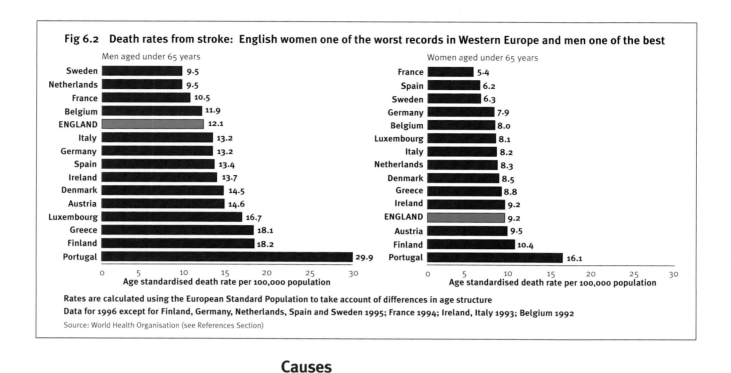

Fig 6.2 Death rates from stroke: English women one of the worst records in Western Europe and men one of the best

Men aged under 65 years

Country	Rate
Sweden	9.5
Netherlands	9.5
France	10.5
Belgium	11.9
ENGLAND	12.1
Italy	13.2
Germany	13.2
Spain	13.4
Ireland	13.7
Denmark	14.5
Austria	14.6
Luxembourg	16.7
Greece	18.1
Finland	18.2
Portugal	29.9

Age standardised death rate per 100,000 population

Women aged under 65 years

Country	Rate
France	5.4
Spain	6.2
Sweden	6.3
Germany	7.9
Belgium	8.0
Luxembourg	8.1
Italy	8.2
Netherlands	8.3
Denmark	8.5
Greece	8.8
Ireland	9.2
ENGLAND	9.2
Austria	9.5
Finland	10.4
Portugal	16.1

Age standardised death rate per 100,000 population

Rates are calculated using the European Standard Population to take account of differences in age structure
Data for 1996 except for Finland, Germany, Netherlands, Spain and Sweden 1995; France 1994; Ireland, Italy 1993; Belgium 1992

Source: World Health Organisation (see References Section)

Causes

'risk factors are unevenly spread across society'

6.4 Several of the major risk factors which increase the chances of people developing coronary heart disease or having a stroke are now well established. The key lifestyle risk factors, shared by coronary heart disease and stroke, are smoking, poor nutrition, obesity, physical inactivity and high blood pressure. Excess alcohol intake is an important additional risk factor for stroke. Many of these risk factors are unevenly spread across society, with poorer people often exposed to the highest risks.

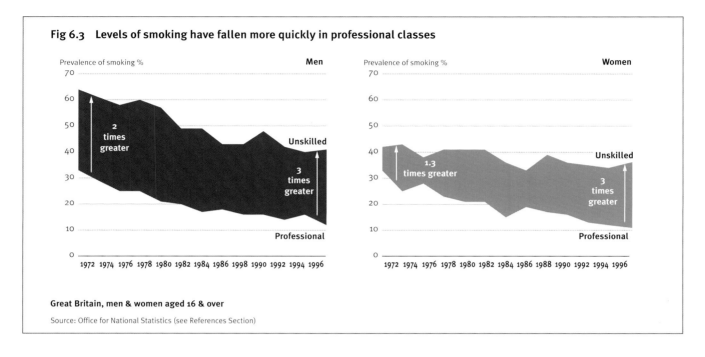

Fig 6.3   Levels of smoking have fallen more quickly in professional classes

Great Britain, men & women aged 16 & over

Source: Office for National Statistics (see References Section)

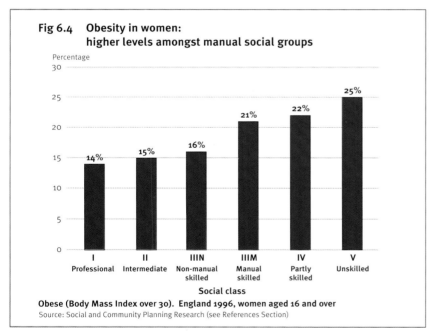

Fig 6.4   Obesity in women: higher levels amongst manual social groups

Obese (Body Mass Index over 30). England 1996, women aged 16 and over

Source: Social and Community Planning Research (see References Section)

6.5 Smoking is the most important modifiable risk factor for coronary heart disease in young and old. The fact that smokers of whatever age, sex or ethnic group have a higher risk of heart attacks than non-smokers has been known for a quarter of a century. All these effects have also been demonstrated in those exposed to other people's smoke (passive smoking). A lifetime non-smoker is 60 per cent less likely than a current smoker to have coronary heart disease and 30 per cent less likely to suffer a stroke.

*'the cycle of social
disadvantage
contributes directly
to the risk of
premature death'*

6.6 While the proportion of young people starting to smoke is similar across social classes, by their 30s half of the better off young people have stopped smoking while three quarters of those in the lowest income group carry on. This is powerful evidence of how the cycle of social disadvantage contributes directly to the risk of premature death, avoidable illness and disability. About one third of smokers are concentrated in the bottom ten per cent of earners in this country. Smoking rates for those in professional social classes have fallen more rapidly than those for the unskilled. For example, in 1972, unskilled men were twice as likely to smoke as professional men; latest figures show that they are now three times as likely to smoke.

6.7 Poor diet – containing too much fat and salt and not enough fruit and vegetables – is another important cause of coronary heart disease and stroke. A diet high in fat, for example, raises cholesterol levels in the blood. A ten per cent reduction in cholesterol lowers the risk of coronary heart disease by 50 per cent at age 40 years falling to 20 per cent at age 70 years. Poor diet is a fact of life for many poorer families. They do not always enjoy easy access to shops selling a variety of affordable foods, which most of us take for granted.

6.8 Keeping physically active provides strong protection against coronary heart disease and stroke. It also has beneficial effects on weight control, blood pressure and diabetes – all of which are risk factors in their own right; protects against brittle bones and maintains muscle power; and increases people's general sense of well-being. Levels of physical activity vary by social group and occupation. People in unskilled occupations are more physically active at work but less so in their leisure time than people in professional occupations. Even so, across all social groups we do too little exercise. Six out of ten men and seven out of ten women are not physically active enough to benefit their health.

6.9 High blood pressure raises significantly the chances of someone having a stroke or developing coronary heart disease. A modest reduction of salt in the diet, reduction in excess alcohol intake or an increase in physical activity could greatly reduce the risk of stroke and significantly reduce the risk of coronary heart disease. Many people with high blood pressure go unrecognised or are treated ineffectively. These people remain at increased risk.

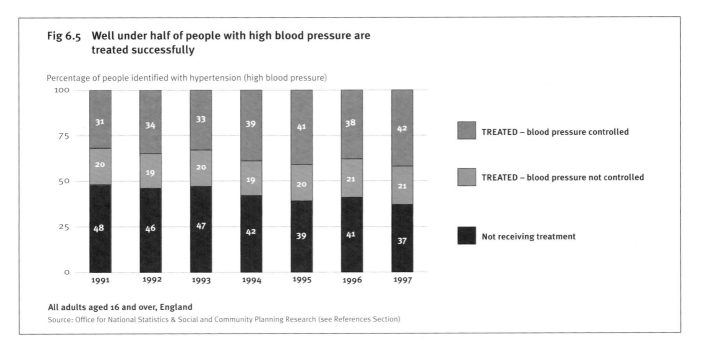

Fig 6.5   Well under half of people with high blood pressure are treated successfully

Percentage of people identified with hypertension (high blood pressure)

TREATED – blood pressure controlled

TREATED – blood pressure not controlled

Not receiving treatment

All adults aged 16 and over, England

Source: Office for National Statistics & Social and Community Planning Research (see References Section)

6.10   There are influences in very early childhood, including while a baby is still in the womb, which determine a person's risk of developing coronary heart disease later in life. For example, small size at birth is an important risk factor for coronary heart disease in adult life. Some argue that these influences are related to nutrition.

6.11   There is mounting evidence of the impact of the underlying causes of coronary heart disease such as income differences. In countries with greater income inequality, health inequality is greater too. And there is evidence that social stress, reflected in the extent to which an individual has low control over his or her job, increases the risk of coronary heart disease and of premature death. Similarly the degree of social cohesion, the strength of social networks in a community and the nature of people's work may all affect their risk of dying from coronary heart disease.

'In countries with greater income inequality, health inequality is greater too'

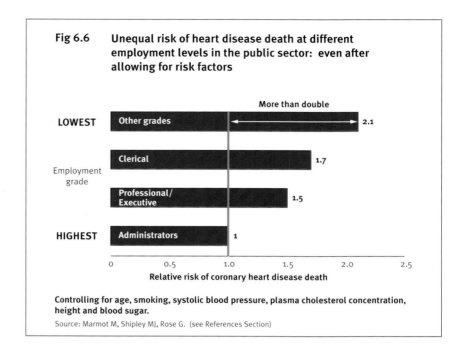

Fig 6.6 **Unequal risk of heart disease death at different employment levels in the public sector: even after allowing for risk factors**

More than double

LOWEST | Other grades ← → 2.1

Employment grade | Clerical 1.7

Professional/ Executive 1.5

HIGHEST | Administrators 1

0   0.5   1.0   1.5   2.0   2.5

Relative risk of coronary heart disease death

Controlling for age, smoking, systolic blood pressure, plasma cholesterol concentration, height and blood sugar.

Source: Marmot M, Shipley MJ, Rose G. (see References Section)

Action: reducing risk and staying healthy

6.12 A number of big changes would put people at much reduced risk of developing coronary heart disease or stroke in the future:

- major changes in diet, particularly among the worst off, with increased consumption of such foods as fruit, vegetables, and oily fish

- large reductions in tobacco smoking particularly among young people, women and people in disadvantaged communities

- people keeping much more physically active – by walking briskly or cycling, for example – on a regular basis

- people controlling their body weight so as to keep to the right level for their physique

- avoiding drinking alcohol to excess

6.13 Deciding not to smoke is choosing life against chronic ill-health and premature death. Giving up smoking produces benefits even in those who have smoked for many years. The White Paper *Smoking Kills* set out our policies for addressing this major cause of stroke and coronary heart disease. In addition to a new three-year public education campaign costing up to £50 million, a network of smoking cessation services will be established around the country, initially in deprived areas known as Health Action Zones. £60 million over three years has been set aside for this vital service. Addiction to nicotine underlies the smoking epidemic and is the reason why people find it so difficult to stop smoking. There is good scientific evidence that a combination of behavioural support and nicotine replacement therapy substantially increases the chances of an ex-smoker remaining free from this addiction. On 17 June we published regulations which set out our intention to ban tobacco advertising with effect from 10 December 1999.

'To ban tobacco advertising from December this year'

Action: more effective treatment

6.14 Early effective treatment of people who are in high risk groups or who have the initial signs of circulatory disease can prevent or delay them developing full blown heart attacks or strokes. Experience shows that people's access to effective treatment is very variable across the country.

6.15 Although we want to prevent as many cases of coronary heart disease as possible, we want to ensure that people who could benefit from operations to relieve their symptoms are able to gain access to these specialist services. In the past we have also seen inequality in access to coronary bypass operations or angioplasty according to where someone happens to live. These operations do not always prolong life but they do improve quality of life, relieve the pain of angina and allow people to live free of disability.

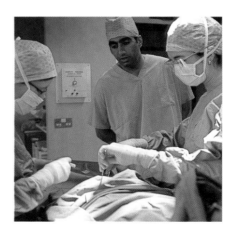

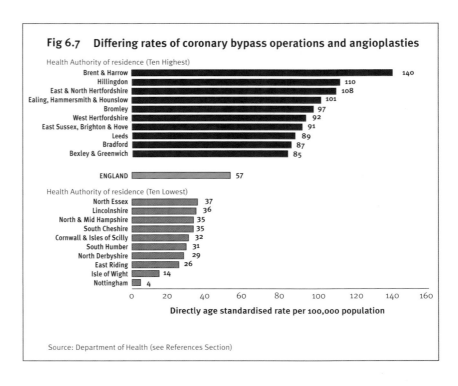

Fig 6.7 Differing rates of coronary bypass operations and angioplasties

Health Authority of residence (Ten Highest)

Health Authority	Rate
Brent & Harrow	140
Hillingdon	110
East & North Hertfordshire	108
Ealing, Hammersmith & Hounslow	101
Bromley	97
West Hertfordshire	92
East Sussex, Brighton & Hove	91
Leeds	89
Bradford	87
Bexley & Greenwich	85
ENGLAND	57

Health Authority of residence (Ten Lowest)

Health Authority	Rate
North Essex	37
Lincolnshire	36
North & Mid Hampshire	35
South Cheshire	35
Cornwall & Isles of Scilly	32
South Humber	31
North Derbyshire	29
East Riding	26
Isle of Wight	14
Nottingham	4

Directly age standardised rate per 100,000 population

Source: Department of Health (see References Section)

'we want to ensure that the standards of the best services in the country apply to all parts of the country'

6.16 Over time we want to ensure that the standards of the best services in the country apply to all parts of the country. That is why we are producing a *National Service Framework for Coronary Heart Disease*. The framework will set national standards and define service models for health promotion, disease prevention, diagnosis, treatment, rehabilitation and care. It will reduce variations in health care and improve service quality and will be published shortly.

6.17 National service frameworks are also planned for older people and for those with diabetes. These will also help to reduce the impact of stroke as well as coronary heart disease. These national service frameworks will be published in April 2000 and April 2001 respectively.

6.18 We are also taking action to improve the control of high blood pressure in the population – too many people remain at risk of heart attack or stroke because their high blood pressure is undetected or treated inadequately.

6.19 To reduce high blood pressure we will:

- through publication of a review of the evidence, promote good practice in GP referrals

- develop an alcohol strategy for publication during 1999

- review the way that high blood pressure is detected and brought under control

- in partnership with the food industry explore the scope for reducing the salt content of processed foods.

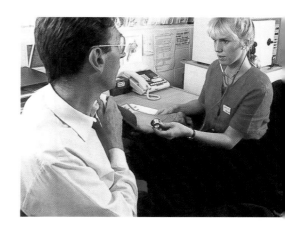

Integrated action

6.20 In our fight against coronary heart disease and stroke we can be successful only if everyone recognises that:

- A whole-generation approach is needed to reduce the impact of such factors as smoking, poor nutrition, obesity and physical inactivity by addressing the importance of influences that operate before birth through healthy pregnancy; laying the foundations for healthy values in early childhood; reinforcing knowledge about risks among young people and equipping them with the skills to take action; helping ensure that in middle and later life people's personal behaviour continues to promote their health and well-being

- Tackling underlying social, economic and environmental conditions is vital. Those factors operate independently as well as through the specific lifestyle factors. So health inequality can be reduced only by giving more people better education; creating employment so that people can achieve greater prosperity; building social capital by increasing social cohesion and reducing social stress by regenerating neighbourhoods and communities; and tackling those aspects of the workplace which are damaging to health

'building social capital by increasing social cohesion and reducing social stress'

- More effective, high quality health services have an important part to play by providing support and advice to people who want to reduce the risks to their health; slowing disease progression in people with early signs and symptoms; limiting long-term incapacity for people who have been ill by well-targeted rehabilitation and follow-up care.

6.21 We will create an integrated strategy for action to reduce the burden of coronary heart disease and stroke through a contract for health. It will identify what the individual citizen must do, what local partnerships will do and what action we will take across Government.

'implementation of the contract by high-level Task Force'

6.22 Our *Healthy Citizens* initiative will help us in this task, through *NHS Direct*; through our *Health Skills* programme – including training for members of the public in the use of defibrillators; and through our *Expert Patients* programme which will enable people with vascular disease to manage their own condition.

6.23 We shall bring together the implementation of this contract for coronary heart disease and stroke with the implementation of the *National Service Framework for Coronary Heart Disease* by setting up a high-level Task Force, accountable to the Chief Medical Officer. The Task Force will ensure that the essential groundwork is laid to set us on course for achieving our target for saving lives which would otherwise be lost to coronary heart disease and stroke. We will identify someone of national prominence to act as its champion, whose function will be to build and maintain momentum for action, to communicate the purpose of the contract and to encourage individuals to commit themselves to it.

6.24 We will use the *Public Health Development Fund* to support the achievement of our target for coronary heart disease and stroke (see paragraphs 11.39 and 11.40).

Fig 6.8 Ways of beating heart disease and stroke: examples of how everyone can play their part

Individuals can...	Local partnerships can...	National Government will...
Stop smoking	Develop smoking cessation services	Continue to make smoking cost more through taxation
Eat more fruit and vegetables	Provide smoke-free environments for non-smokers	Enable access to a range of services including outlets for food and physical activity
Be physically active for at least half an hour 5 days a week	Improve access to adequate food retail services	Promote safe travel to school and encourage opportunities for more walking and cycling as modes of transport
Drink sensibly	Promote safe travel to school	Develop a strategy to promote sensible drinking
Take medication as prescribed	Promote healthy catering in schools and hospitals	Develop nutritional standards for school meals
Maintain a healthy weight	Implement National Service Frameworks for Coronary Heart Disease, Diabetes and Older People	Develop National Service Frameworks on Coronary Heart Disease, Diabetes and Older People
Have blood pressure checked regularly		

Contribution to target reduction in deaths from circulatory disease by 2010 saving up to

200,000
lives in total

40%

Cut in death rate from circulatory disease in people aged under 75 years, between 1997 and 2010

7 Saving lives: accidents

'Accidental injury puts more children in hospital than any other cause'

Target: to reduce the death rates from accidents by at least one fifth and to reduce the rate of serious injury from accidents by at least one tenth by 2010 – saving up to 12,000 lives in total

7.1 Accidents are responsible for 10,000 deaths a year across England. Accidental injury heads the league tables of causes of death among children and young people in England, Europe and America. It puts more children in hospital than any other cause. Accidental injury has in the past been one of the most neglected areas for preventive action, the commissioning of research and the education and training of health professionals.

How do we compare?

7.2 We have lower death rates from road accidents in this country than in most other European countries. We have seen substantial falls in the rate of children killed in accidents over the last 25 years. In our drive for a healthier nation, these and similar figures are encouraging.

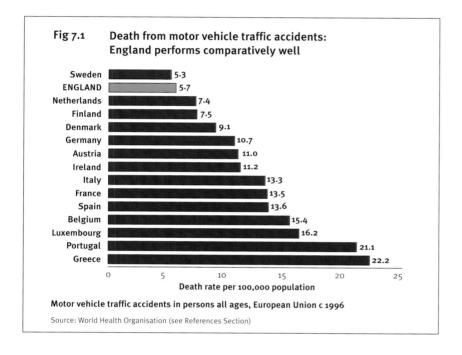

Fig 7.1   Death from motor vehicle traffic accidents: England performs comparatively well

Country	Death rate
Sweden	5.3
ENGLAND	5.7
Netherlands	7.4
Finland	7.5
Denmark	9.1
Germany	10.7
Austria	11.0
Ireland	11.2
Italy	13.3
France	13.5
Spain	13.6
Belgium	15.4
Luxembourg	16.2
Portugal	21.1
Greece	22.2

Death rate per 100,000 population

Motor vehicle traffic accidents in persons all ages, European Union c 1996

Source: World Health Organisation (see References Section)

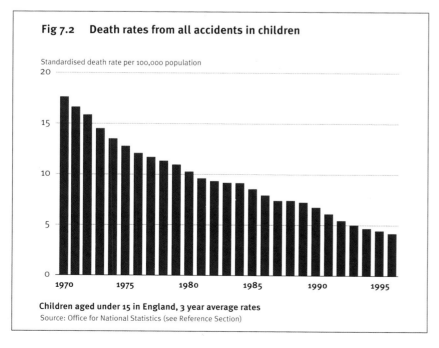

Fig 7.2   Death rates from all accidents in children

Standardised death rate per 100,000 population

Children aged under 15 in England, 3 year average rates

Source: Office for National Statistics (see Reference Section)

'road accidents and serious injuries are more severe on our rural roads'

7.3 But in other areas the record is less good. Rates of death in childhood from pedestrian accidents in this country are amongst the highest in Europe. And, as children grow up, deaths from accidental injury account for a greater proportion of all childhood deaths. Among older people the rate of deaths from falls is not coming down. There are also substantial differences in deaths from accidents across the United Kingdom. For example, road accidents and serious injuries are more severe on our rural roads than in other areas.

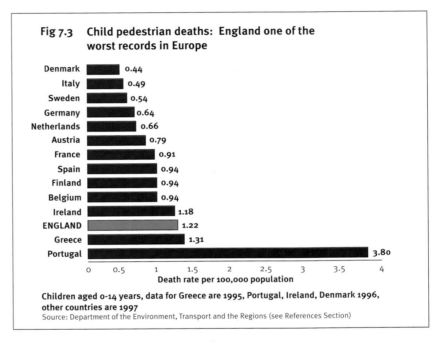

Fig 7.3 Child pedestrian deaths: England one of the worst records in Europe

Children aged 0-14 years, data for Greece are 1995, Portugal, Ireland, Denmark 1996, other countries are 1997
Source: Department of the Environment, Transport and the Regions (see References Section)

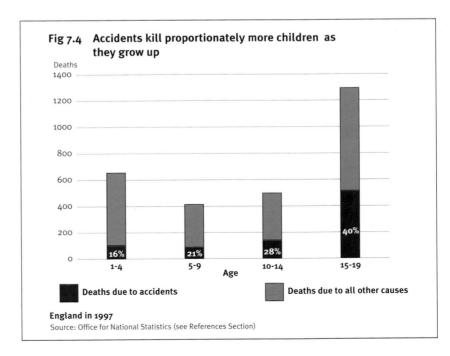

Fig 7.4 Accidents kill proportionately more children as they grow up

England in 1997
Source: Office for National Statistics (see References Section)

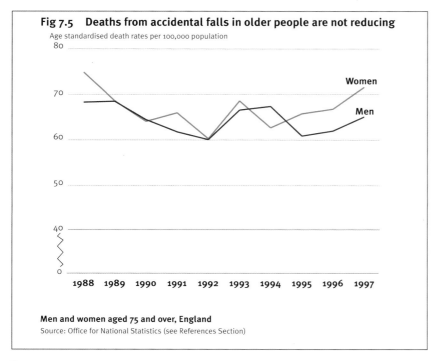

Fig 7.5   Deaths from accidental falls in older people are not reducing

Age standardised death rates per 100,000 population

Men and women aged 75 and over, England

Source: Office for National Statistics (see References Section)

Causes

7.4 Road traffic accidents are a principal cause of accidental death and injury. Across the whole population in 1997, 3,559 people were killed, 42,967 were seriously injured and 280,978 were slightly injured in road traffic accidents. Every year 1,500 car drivers and adult passengers die in road accidents and one hundred times that number are injured. And every year 1,000 or so adult pedestrians and cyclists are killed and 40,000 are injured. Motorcyclists are at the highest risk of all. In 1997 for every 100 million kilometres travelled, 150 motorcyclists were killed or seriously injured compared with 89 cyclists and 4 car drivers.

7.5 Families can be destroyed by the loss of parents and breadwinners. But children's deaths are the most tragic waste of life. Despite the improvements, road traffic accidents remain the biggest single cause of accidental death amongst children and young people. Each year in England nearly 180 children die and almost 4,800 are injured as pedestrians or cyclists. Many are killed when playing or walking close to their own homes. Added to this are the 215 deaths and 2,690 or more serious injuries to children riding as car passengers.

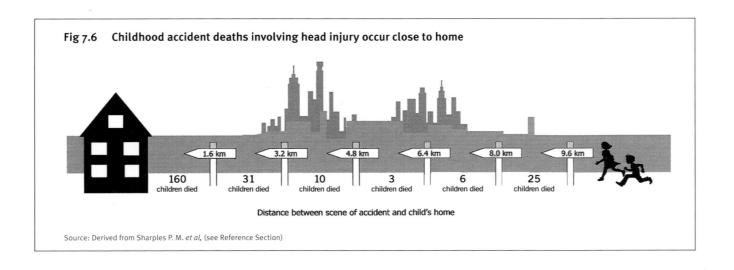

Fig 7.6   Childhood accident deaths involving head injury occur close to home

1.6 km	3.2 km	4.8 km	6.4 km	8.0 km	9.6 km
160 children died	**31** children died	**10** children died	**3** children died	**6** children died	**25** children died

Distance between scene of accident and child's home

Source: Derived from Sharples P. M. *et al*, (see Reference Section)

'The younger the child, the greater the risk'

7.6 Older people are at particular risk of death and disability from falls. Osteoporosis (brittle bones) affects more people, especially women, as they grow older and can be a cause of accidents and contribute to the severity of those accidents. Broken wrists and hips become more likely and can mean lengthy hospital stays, creating long term health and social care needs for the individual.

7.7 One third of all accidents to adults occur in the home. Many are linked with people falling or stumbling in the home. Over 3,000 people aged over 65 years are killed annually in falls. The home is also the setting for many serious accidents to children from a variety of causes: fires, burns, drowning, choking, poisoning and cuts from sharp objects. The younger the child, the greater the risk. About half of all deaths among children under 5 happen in the home.

7.8 Some occupations expose employees to greater potential risks than others. Those risks may take different forms. Some may be linked to the work environment, such as mining or quarrying, or with work processes such as those involving poisonous substances. Others are associated with a failure to manage risk, such as falls from a height or from moving vehicles, in the construction industry, for example. Controls for risks are covered in legislation and enforced by the Health and Safety Executive and local authorities. Over decades the number of accidents in these areas has fallen markedly. But there were still nearly 140 fatal accidents in the construction industry and agriculture combined in 1997-8. The *Self-Reported Work-Related Illness Survey* for 1995 concluded that about 2 million people suffered from ill-health either caused or made worse by their work.

7.9 People use their leisure time in a whole variety of ways. Many choose to be physically active, which helps them to reduce the risk of coronary heart disease. Yet these activities also bring some risk of accidental injury. Every year about 800,000 people are injured while playing sport, 215,000 of them children.

Action: reducing risk and staying healthy

7.10 We can all do a great deal to contain these risks of accidental injury. Sometimes it is a matter of taking simple precautions, such as remembering to wear a seatbelt. Sometimes it is a question of a better product design or the development of better controls.

7.11 We will reduce accidents by making the environment safer. We will reduce road traffic accidents through more careful planning of traffic flows; through traffic calming measures; by an effective speed management policy; and through encouraging the design of vehicles in ways which offer better protection not just to the occupants but also to others involved in collisions. We will do more to improve conditions and give greater priority to pedestrians and cyclists, including by designing safer routes to school through school travel plans. We will make sure our traffic management policies are best suited to their locations, whether urban or rural. The forthcoming *Road Safety Strategy* will set out in detail how we will make our roads safer.

'give greater priority to pedestrians and cyclists'

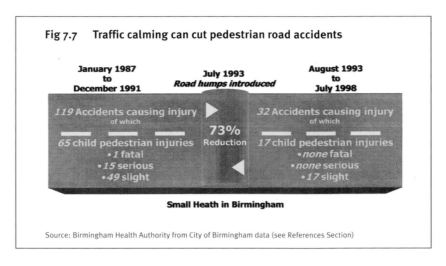

Fig 7.7   Traffic calming can cut pedestrian road accidents

January 1987 to December 1991	July 1993 Road humps introduced	August 1993 to July 1998
119 Accidents causing injury of which	73% Reduction	32 Accidents causing injury of which
65 child pedestrian injuries • 1 fatal • 15 serious • 49 slight		17 child pedestrian injuries • none fatal • none serious • 17 slight

Small Heath in Birmingham

Source: Birmingham Health Authority from City of Birmingham data (see References Section)

7.12 Careful design is important to minimise the risk of accidents in the home. For new homes, Building Regulations set standards for the design of the main features associated with accidents. These include stairs, balconies and the use of safety glass in doors and low-level windows.

7.13 In the playground accidents could be reduced through more careful equipment design, the use of soft materials as flooring, and more supervision.

7.14 Drownings in canals, rivers, ponds and swimming pools could be reduced through the use of barriers which restrict access, through more teaching of swimming and through more adult supervision.

7.15 We can also reduce accidents through safer behaviour. Road safety training has long been a feature of childhood, and there is evidence that training parents and children together is particularly effective. We have introduced a practical training manual for children called *Kerbcraft*, based on a successful road safety education scheme run originally in Drumchapel in Glasgow.

7.16 All of us can play a role in improving safety for other road users by driving safely, following the Highway Code. Cyclists can reduce risks to themselves by using safe cycle routes where they exist, and by taking part in cycling skills training courses.

7.17 Many parents discourage their children from walking and cycling precisely because they are worried about the dangers from traffic. But in using private cars more we are restricting not only children's physical well-being but also their social development. Unless they have the chance to learn early on how to make decisions for themselves, children may eventually be at more risk on the roads and in other public places. Our *Safer Travel to School* initiative will encourage more children to walk or cycle to school.

7.18 Many accidents in the home can be prevented by taking simple precautions. The Department of Trade and Industry is conducting a three-year campaign targeted at older people, their families and carers setting out a few simple and practical steps which will help to prevent falls in the home – the biggest cause of accidental deaths in the home, and one which affects millions of people. The Department of Trade and Industry is also actively promoting safety advice on a range of other home safety topics, including gardening, carbon monoxide poisoning and burns and scalds.

7.19 We can encourage people to adopt safer behaviour which makes injury less likely by increasing awareness of the causes of accidents in the home, in leisure, and in the workplace; and what can be done to make them safer. For example, when the Department of Trade and Industry ran its campaign on firework safety in 1998, focusing on sparkler safety, injuries from sparklers dropped by 36 per cent.

7.20 Safety protection is another effective way of preventing accidental injury. Seat belts and child restraints have been shown to be effective in reducing deaths and the severity of injuries to occupants of road vehicles. Cycle helmets have been shown to reduce the risk of head injuries among cyclists by as much as 85 per cent. Smoke alarms have been shown to reduce the number of deaths and injuries from fires significantly. One recent study estimated that an 80 per cent reduction was achieved in the incidence of injuries from residential fires. People can make their enjoyment of sport freer of injuries by taking simple precautions suitable to the sport.

Action: more effe[...] [...]ment

frontline ambulances now have a fully qualified paramedic'

7.21 To improve tre[...] [...] those who suffer accidental injury there must be fast, effective action at all levels from the time the injury occurs to the initial diagnosis and treatment and to the after-care. The physical and psychological injuries caused by accidents will be considered within the *National Service Framework for Older People.*

7.22 We have seen in the past the ways in which the sequence of events in response to accidental injury has been broken. Examples of ambulances failing to arrive in the critical time after a serious accident. Examples of children with serious injury lying too long in a local hospital whilst a bed is found in a specialist centre. Examples of failures to draw up good care plans leading to people with head injury not reaching their full recovery potential. These are the exceptions. But they must not be allowed to happen.

7.23 Frontline ambulances responding to 999 calls now have a fully qualified paramedic as well as a trained technician. Their training includes basic and advanced life support as well as a range of interventions which may be needed by people injured in accidents. Recent work indicates that patients cared for by paramedics recover better than patients who are not.

7.24 Following the 1997 Report *Paediatric Intensive Care: A Framework for the Future,* the Government has invested an additional £20 million in children's intensive care to ensure that critically ill children – for example, those suffering from head injury, burns or poisoning – can be swiftly transferred to a specialised centre accompanied by specially trained doctors and nurses. This aims to avoid past tragedies where staff and facilities were not available for such emergencies.

7.25 We are developing policies designed to ensure prompt and effective rehabilitation, treatment and care, to maximise people's recovery from accidental injury.

Integrated action

7.26 In our fight against accidental injury we can be successful only if everyone recognises that:

- There are key age groups that must be targeted. In particular, the greatest gain in lives saved and disability prevented would result from reducing injury (or its severity) in children up to 15 years (especially those from manual and unskilled households); in young people aged 16-24 years involved in road traffic accidents; and in older people who are at risk of stumbling or falling

- There are special factors associated with each different type of environment in which accidental injury occurs: the risks of death and injury can be reduced if the 'accident prone' features of roads, houses, workplaces, playgrounds and other settings are carefully analysed and measures designed specifically to reduce risk

- Single interventions will seldom be successful. A co-ordinated approach is needed. Individuals can take action for themselves and others. Transport, land use, housing, social and economic policies can all be harnessed together in ways which can reduce significantly the incidence of accidental injury.

7.27 Besides this, our *Healthy Citizens* programme will help to minimise the effects of accidents through our *Health Skills* programme for 14 –16 year-olds and for adults.

7.28 We will set up a high-level Task Force, accountable to the Chief Medical Officer, to oversee the first year of implementation of the contract to ensure that the essential groundwork is undertaken to set us on course for achieving the target. We will identify a person of national prominence to act as its champion, whose function will be to build and maintain momentum for action, to communicate the purpose of the contract and to engage people in it.

7.29 We will use the *Public Health Development Fund* to support the achievement of our target for accidental injury.

Fig 7.8 Ways of beating accidental injury: examples of how everyone can play their part.

Individuals can...	Local partnerships can...	National Government will...
Install and maintain smoke alarms	Conduct a "safer community" audit	Co-ordinate government strategy
Improve driver behaviour	Introduce area wide road safety measures	Revise road safety targets
Maintain a physically active lifestyle	Develop local safe routes to school	Promote safer travel to school
Use safety devices in the home and at work	Help people at higher risk to modify their homes	Educate the public and professionals on falls prevention
Avoid drinking and driving	Increase smoke alarm ownership	Review housing fitness standards
Learn resuscitation skills	Provide prompt emergency treatment to accident victims	Promote fire safety

Contribution to target reduction in deaths from accidents by 2010 saving up to

12,000

lives in total

20%

Cut in death rate from accidents between 1997 and 2010

These steps will also contribute to our target of a 10 per cent reduction in serious injury from accidents

8 Saving lives: mental health

Target:[1] to reduce the death rate from suicide and undetermined injury by at least a fifth by 2010 – saving up to 4,000 lives in total

8.1 Mental health is as important to an individual as good physical health. Mental health influences how we feel, perceive, think, communicate and understand. Without good mental health, people can be unable to fulfil their full potential or play an active part in everyday life.

8.2 Mental health problems are a major cause of ill-health, disability and mortality. They include:

[1] In the Green Paper we proposed suicide as a proxy target to cover the whole of the mental health priority area. A number of responses to the consultation suggested that a morbidity target would be better but none could offer solutions to the problems of measuring and monitoring such a target. A suicide target has the advantages of reliable data, while many mental health policies, including those to promote good mental health, will lead to reductions in suicides.

- depression and anxiety – extremely common in both urban and rural areas, often disabling and may last a long time if untreated

- schizophrenia – relatively rare but often extremely severe, disabling and long-term

- bipolar affective disorder (formerly known as manic depression) – relatively rare, episodic in nature and often very severe

- dementia – common in older people, involving progressive deterioration of intellectual and social functioning, with no recovery

- anti-social personality disorder – which contributes to crime and aggression.

'unemployed people are twice as likely to suffer from depression as people in work'

8.3 People with mental illness may have difficulties in sustaining supportive relationships with friends, family and colleagues; with parenting; with work and other daily activities. They may have higher rates of substance misuse. These social consequences of mental illness increase the stigma and social exclusion suffered by people with mental illness and that, in turn, makes the original condition worse.

8.4 More people who are worse off financially and socially, particularly in inner cities, have mental illness; more contemplate suicide and more actually commit suicide than people who are better off. For example:

- unemployed people are twice as likely to suffer from depression as people in work

- children in the poorest households are three times more likely to have mental ill-health than children in the best-off households

- people sleeping rough or using night shelters are four times more likely to have a mental disorder than the general population

- people in prisons are at least fifteen times more likely to have a psychotic disorder than the general population

- refugees have higher rates of mental disorder than the general population.

8.5 In England, on average, more than one person dies every two hours as a result of suicide. Suicidal thoughts are quite common but are seldom acted on. But if a quick and lethal method of suicide is readily at hand someone might act impulsively without allowing time for second thoughts or rescue. So there are more suicides among those who have easy access to the means of killing themselves such as guns, certain medicines or chemicals. That is one of the reasons why suicide figures are high for some professional groups such as doctors, nurses, farmers, vets and pharmacists.

'mental illness has a high economic cost'

8.6 Many people are mentally ill die prematurely from physical illness, especially respiratory illness, cancer or coronary heart disease. People with eating disorders and those involved in substance misuse are at highest risk, although the risks are almost as great for those with schizophrenia or major depression.

8.7 People with mental illness may suffer considerable fear, mental pain and distress, sometimes for many years, taking a considerable toll on themselves and their families. They may be socially excluded because of their mental illness. Besides the immense cost in personal suffering which mental illness carries, it has a high economic cost as well. A recent study estimated that the cost in England amounted to £32.1 billion.

How do we compare?

8.8 Suicide rates within the UK are reasonably similar in England, Wales and Northern Ireland but are higher in Scotland. Suicide rates in England are among the lowest in the European Union.

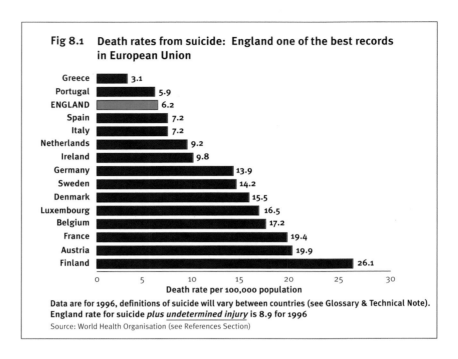

Fig 8.1   Death rates from suicide: England one of the best records in European Union

Country	Death rate per 100,000 population
Greece	3.1
Portugal	5.9
ENGLAND	6.2
Spain	7.2
Italy	7.2
Netherlands	9.2
Ireland	9.8
Germany	13.9
Sweden	14.2
Denmark	15.5
Luxembourg	16.5
Belgium	17.2
France	19.4
Austria	19.9
Finland	26.1

Death rate per 100,000 population

Data are for 1996, definitions of suicide will vary between countries (see Glossary & Technical Note). England rate for suicide *plus underdetermined injury* is 8.9 for 1996

Source: World Health Organisation (see References Section)

Causes

8.9 Detailed research on the causes of mental illness has shown that the major risk factors for mental illness include:

- poverty, poor education, unemployment

- social isolation stemming from discrimination against people with all types of physical disabilities

- major life events such as bereavement, redundancy, financial problems, being the victim of crime

- genetic predisposition

- drug and alcohol misuse

- developmental factors such as foetal damage and injury at birth

- poor parenting.

Action: promoting good mental health and reducing risk

8.10 Promoting good mental health is relevant to everyone. We can all enhance our mental well-being through some simple steps which make it easier for us to cope with the problems and pressures of daily life. These can be as straightforward as keeping in touch with our family and friends, and keeping involved with our local community. Making time for relaxation and for physical activity can reduce stress, while asking for help and talking problems over can also prevent mental health problems from building up.

8.11 We are promoting these simple steps through national public education campaigns, for use in a wide range of settings. Schools, workplaces, neighbourhoods and prisons should all play their part in improving mental health as well as improving health generally.

8.12 In addition it is possible to reduce the risk of various mental illnesses, such as depression by strengthening support systems; dementia by stopping smoking, adopting a healthy diet and being physically active; relapse in schizophrenia by specific family interventions; and suicide through a range of specific measures.

'it is possible to reduce the risk of various mental illnesses'

8.13 For example unemployed people are less likely to suffer depression and to have better success finding work if they are given social support and help in developing job-seeking skills; people caring for relatives with dementia are less likely to suffer from depression if they are given practical information about the disease. Similarly people caring for relatives with schizophrenia benefit from practical information and social support; support groups supplying a combination of practical help, social networking and advice on parenting have also been proven to have a dramatic impact on the mental health of young isolated mothers and on the cognitive and emotional development of their pre-school children. Rapid treatment for depressed mothers can prevent harm to the children who may otherwise experience cognitive and emotional damage. Self-help support groups have proved beneficial for widows where they can offer each other one-to-one support alongside other practical help and small group meetings. Children at school with unrecognised learning difficulties including dyslexia will benefit from appropriate school programmes for assessment and help.

campaign against living miserably
0800 58 58 58

CALM – The Campaign Against Living Miserably

CALM is a pilot helpline in Manchester, funded by the Department of Health, offering a safety net for young men with mental ill-health. It aims to tackle the stigma attached to depression and mental illness and encourage take-up of the services available. It is staffed by trained counsellors who offer advice, guidance and information. We are looking to build on the success of *CALM* by making the helpline available in other areas, in partnership with local agencies and authorities.

Children whose parents are divorcing can benefit from school-based help and parents can be taught parenting skills.

8.14 We can reduce suicide through the following steps:

- reduce access to methods of suicide, such as controlling the pack sizes for paracetamol available off the shelf

- develop *NHS Direct,* networked to specialist mental health helplines, as a source of advice for those in mental distress

- good assessment and follow-up of people who attempt to kill themselves

- use good practice guidelines on looking after suicidal people in primary and specialist care

- continue professional training about prompt detection, assessment, diagnosis and treatment of depression and assessment of suicidal risk

- support people who are at high risk of suicide, particularly people with severe mental illness and those in high risk occupations

- develop mental health promotion strategies in schools, workplaces and prisons which enhance social support and coping strategies and which tackle bullying

- work with the media to ensure responsible reporting of suicides which neither glamorises the event nor publishes the method used

- audit suicides in order to learn the lessons for prevention. We support the *National Confidential Inquiry into Suicide and Homicide* which audits suicides across the country.

Action: early recognition

8.15 There are far more people with a mental health problem than the specialist services see. Some of them will seek help from families and friends. Many will be seen by their family doctor but mental health problems can be difficult to diagnose, especially when the patient has physical symptoms or learning difficulties or if there is a language or other cultural barrier. On average, family doctors identify only about half of the people who come to them with depression and anxiety, and not all of those receive the right treatment. Some patients first come into contact with the police or social services rather than a hospital or a family doctor. For all these reasons it is important that people in the relevant agencies, especially those in the health service, have the skills to recognise the symptoms of mental illness.

8.16 Mental health is the subject of one of the first two new National Service Frameworks. The Framework will set national standards and define service models for mental health promotion, suicide prevention, assessment, diagnosis, treatment, rehabilitation and care. We shall use the Framework to ensure that these professional staff have the skills to detect early signs of mental illness and to assess suicidal risk; and we are ensuring that mental health teams have the necessary skills for relapse prevention, including for those with concomitant substance misuse.

'the National Service Framework will set national standards and define service models for mental health'

Action: effective treatment

8.17 We can achieve a great deal by promoting good mental health, preventing illness and by prompt and effective treatment in primary care. Our *Healthy Citizens* initiative will help individuals to take control of their own mental health, through making use of *NHS Direct,* through developing their health skills and through our *Expert Patients* programme. But there will always be a need for effective specialist mental health services. Access to specialist treatment and care varies across the country as well as by age, ethnic group, gender, and social class. We therefore need to ensure that people suffering from mental ill-health have access to consistently high quality treatment and care services suited to their needs. To achieve this, in December 1998 we published

Modernising Mental Health Services – safe, sound and supportive, setting out in detail our strategy for ensuring effective mental health services. That strategy made mental health a national priority across both health and social care services.

8.18 Secondly we have launched a fundamental review of the law on mental health to ensure that it is brought up-to-date to reflect modern practice. It will report in the summer.

8.19 Thirdly the *National Service Framework for Mental Health,* to be implemented from April 2000, will ensure the development of consistent high quality services which cross professional and agency boundaries, and which are equally accessible to all.

Integrated action

8.20 If we are to promote mental health and reduce not only mental illness but also its adverse impact on individuals and families we need to:

- ensure that mental health is regarded as a key outcome of each strand of the Government's agenda to promote social inclusion – from *Sure Start* to *Better Government for Older People;* from the *Rough Sleepers Initiative* to the *Welfare to Work* programme, and across the range of local initiatives

- put in place the range of action to reduce suicide – within the NHS and partner agencies, the media and those who can help to reduce access to the methods of suicide

- strengthen the capacity of primary care services to identify, assess and treat those with mental health problems

- ensure effective care for those with severe mental illness; and better support for those who care for them.

8.21 The *National Service Framework for Mental Health* will cover these areas – setting out standards and service models with a clear drive towards implementation and delivery. It will be a key element in meeting our target for reducing suicides. It will address the whole

'strengthen the capacity of primary care services'

range of mental health service provision, from primary care, where the majority of mental health problems can be managed, through to specialist mental health services. This will help to ensure that people with mental health problems receive the service they need, regardless of who they are or where they live.

8.22 We shall bring together the implementation of this contract for mental health with the delivery of the *National Service Framework for Mental Health* by setting up a high-level Task Force, accountable to the Chief Medical Officer. The Task Force will ensure that the essential ground work is laid to set us on course for achieving our target for saving lives which would otherwise be lost to suicide. We will identify someone of national prominence to act as its champion, whose function will be to build and maintain momentum for action, to communicate the purpose of the contract and to encourage individuals to commit themselves to it.

8.23 We will use the *Public Health Development Fund* to support the achievement of our target for mental health.

Fig 8.2 Ways of beating mental health problems: examples of how everyone can play their part

Individuals can...	Local partnerships can...	National Government will...
Support others at times of stress	Implement National Service Framework	Publish Mental Health National Service Framework
Better their lives through using education/training/employment opportunities	Encourage development of healthy schools and workplaces	Invest more resources in mental health services
Use opportunities for relaxation and physical exercise	Develop local support networks – culture, age and gender sensitive – which meet needs of high risk groups	Improve employment opportunities through *Welfare to Work*
Drink sensibly and avoid illegal drugs	Improve community safety	Develop strategy to promote sensible drinking and implement anti drugs strategy
Increase their understanding of what good mental health is	Develop effective housing strategies	Reduce homelessness through Rough Sleepers Initiative
Contact help quickly when difficulties start	Encourage open and green space for children and families, and other leisure facilities	Promote pre-school education and educational achievement
Contribute information to service planners and get involved	Identify local resources and services, and help them to work in partnership	Consider mental as well as physical health impact when developing wider government policies

Contribution to target reduction in deaths from mental health problems (suicide) by 2010 saving up to

4,000
lives in total

20%

Cut in death rate from suicide between 1997 and 2010

9 Public health: wider action

9.1 Our four priority areas address a wide range of public health issues, but there are further important threats to our health. We are tackling these as well, in a series of strategies complementary to *Saving lives: Our Healthier Nation* sharing its overall aims and focusing on specific problems. Like this strategy for health, they rely on Government-wide action and shared responsibility.

Sexual health

9.2 In March we announced our plans to draw up a national strategy for sexual health which will encourage the development of more comprehensive sex and relationships education, more coherent health promotion messages and more effective service interventions.

9.3 Sexual health is an important public health issue. England has one of the highest teenage conception rates in the developed world and the highest in Western Europe. Such rates vary in severity round the country, with some local authority areas such as Wear Valley having conception rates for girls under 16 as high as 22 in every 1,000. Babies born to teenage mothers have death rates 50 per cent higher than the national average. Many young girls who fall pregnant and choose to keep their baby are likely to experience poverty and poor health and pass such disadvantages onto the next generation.

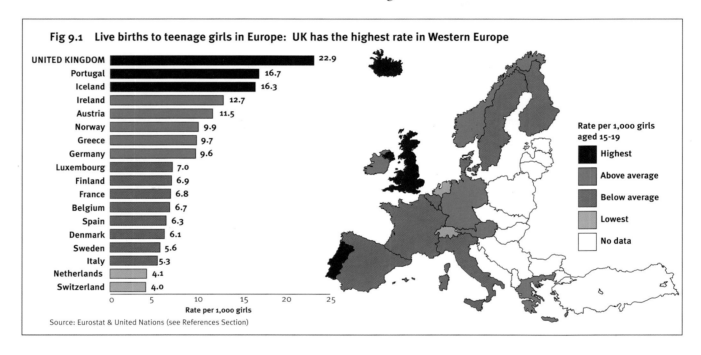

Fig 9.1 Live births to teenage girls in Europe: UK has the highest rate in Western Europe

Country	Rate per 1,000 girls
UNITED KINGDOM	22.9
Portugal	16.7
Iceland	16.3
Ireland	12.7
Austria	11.5
Norway	9.9
Greece	9.7
Germany	9.6
Luxembourg	7.0
Finland	6.9
France	6.8
Belgium	6.7
Spain	6.3
Denmark	6.1
Sweden	5.6
Italy	5.3
Netherlands	4.1
Switzerland	4.0

Rate per 1,000 girls

Rate per 1,000 girls aged 15-19

- Highest
- Above average
- Below average
- Lowest
- No data

Source: Eurostat & United Nations (see References Section)

'clear goal to cut the rate of teenage conceptions by half in under-18s by 2010'

9.4 Action is already in hand on a number of fronts. The Prime Minister asked the Social Exclusion Unit to develop an integrated strategy to cut rates of teenage parenthood and propose better solutions to combat the risk of social exclusion for vulnerable teenage parents and their children. Its Report set out an action plan comprising:

- a national campaign to mobilise every section of the community to achieve its clear goal to cut the rate of teenage conceptions by half in under-18s by 2010

- better prevention by tackling the underlying causes of teenage pregnancy through better education about sex and relationships, clearer messages about contraception and special attention to high-risk groups including young men

- better support for young teenagers and teenage parents to ensure they finish their education and learn parenting skills; and changes to the housing rules so that young, 16–17 year-old teenagers will no longer be housed in independent tenancies but in supervised accommodation offering the support they need.

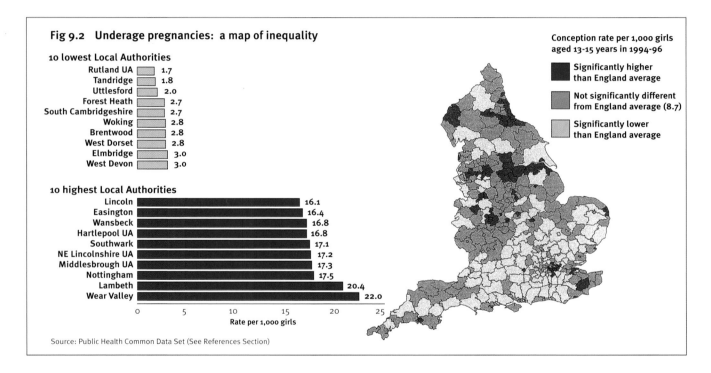

Fig 9.2   Underage pregnancies: a map of inequality

Conception rate per 1,000 girls aged 13-15 years in 1994-96

- Significantly higher than England average
- Not significantly different from England average (8.7)
- Significantly lower than England average

10 lowest Local Authorities

Local Authority	Rate
Rutland UA	1.7
Tandridge	1.8
Uttlesford	2.0
Forest Heath	2.7
South Cambridgeshire	2.7
Woking	2.8
Brentwood	2.8
West Dorset	2.8
Elmbridge	3.0
West Devon	3.0

10 highest Local Authorities

Local Authority	Rate
Lincoln	16.1
Easington	16.4
Wansbeck	16.8
Hartlepool UA	16.8
Southwark	17.1
NE Lincolnshire UA	17.2
Middlesbrough UA	17.3
Nottingham	17.5
Lambeth	20.4
Wear Valley	22.0

Rate per 1,000 girls

Source: Public Health Common Data Set (See References Section)

9.5 Sexually transmitted infections are increasing, particularly chlamydia and gonorrhoea (which can result in infertility), and particularly among teenagers. For 16-19 year-olds there was a 53 per cent increase in cases of gonorrhoea between 1995 and 1997, and 45 per cent for chlamydia. In 1997 there were nearly half a million new diagnoses of sexually transmitted infections in genito-urinary medicine clinics alone.

9.6 Chlamydia is the single most preventable cause of infertility in women, and screening pilots are underway. A national screening programme will be considered when results are available from these pilots. And there are a number of public health promotion campaigns for young people which aim to increase their understanding of sexually transmitted infections and how to prevent them.

'support for teenage parents to ensure they finish their education and learn parenting skills'

107

'forthcoming HIV/AIDS strategy will cover testing and treatment as well as prevention'

9.7 HIV infection and AIDS remain serious threats to health. Because of early prevention efforts we have fared better than many other European countries. France, for example, has four times as many people with HIV as the UK. But we cannot be complacent. Last year saw the highest number of new HIV infections ever in the UK at nearly 3,000, almost twice the figure of a decade ago. So we must continue to promote messages about safer sex, both to the general public and those specific groups who are at particular risk of HIV infection. While new treatments are improving both the length and quality of life for HIV patients, there is still no vaccine or cure. And there are signs that some patients may not respond well to the new drugs, particularly over long periods. So our forthcoming HIV/AIDS strategy will cover issues of testing and treatment as well as prevention. It will be developed within the frameworks set out in *The new NHS* and *Modernising Social Services*.

Tackling Drugs to Build a Better Britain

9.8 Drug misuse is associated with poor health both directly, for example through the effect of overdoses and the spread of infection (specifically HIV/AIDS and hepatitis B and C); and indirectly, because of the link with social exclusion through homelessness, poverty, unemployment and criminal behaviour. And the problem is frighteningly widespread.

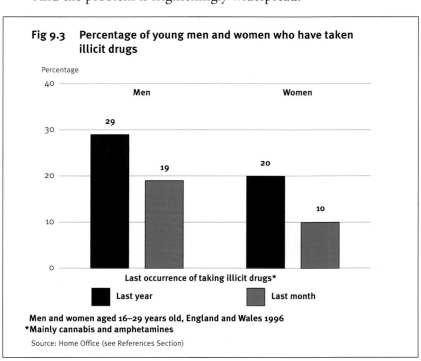

Fig 9.3 Percentage of young men and women who have taken illicit drugs

Percentage

Men   Women

Last occurrence of taking illicit drugs*

■ Last year   ■ Last month

Men and women aged 16–29 years old, England and Wales 1996
*Mainly cannabis and amphetamines

Source: Home Office (see References Section)

9.9 In *Tackling Drugs to Build a Better Britain*, published last year, we signalled our goal of shifting resources from dealing with the consequences of drug misuse to prevention and treatment. Our aims are to:

- help young people to resist drug misuse

- protect our communities from drug-related anti-social and criminal behaviour

- enable people with drug-related problems to overcome them and live healthy, crime-free lives

- stifle the availability of illegal drugs.

'shifting resources from dealing with the consequences of drug misuse to prevention and treatment'

9.10 Success will require concerted action at every level. At national level, the policies of different Government Departments are being brought together by the UK Anti-Drugs Co-ordinator, matched at local level by the Drug Action Teams on which a range of agencies are represented.

9.11 In May the UK Anti-Drugs Co-ordinator published his first Annual Report and Action Plan setting out his key performance targets for the next 10 years.

Alcohol

9.12 Moderate alcohol consumption is a part of everyday life for many, bringing enjoyment and relaxation. For older people, drinking small amounts of alcohol can give some protection against coronary heart disease. But heavy drinking is harmful not only to individuals, but also to their families and to society at large. As well as directly causing illness such as cirrhosis of the liver, alcohol contributes to certain cancers and to stroke. Its misuse places families under stress, sometimes resulting in domestic violence, mental illness, and family break-up. Alcohol-related disorder and violence affect the wider community. It is a factor in many accidents.

Figure 9.4

Some of the most common adverse health effects of heavy alcohol consumption

- liver cirrhosis and liver cancer

- mouth, throat, gullet and possibly breast cancer

- high blood pressure and related conditions such as heart and kidney disease, and stroke

- complications in pregnancy and infancy

- mental illness, suicide, epilepsy and damage to the nervous system

- accidents

- violence

Source: Department of Health (see References Section)

'An effective strategy to tackle alcohol misuse in the year 2000'

9.13 In the Green Paper *Our Healthier Nation* we undertook to develop a new strategy to tackle alcohol misuse. Our broad aims are:

- to encourage people who drink to do so sensibly in line with our guidance, so as to avoid alcohol-related problems

- to protect individuals and communities from anti-social and criminal behaviour related to alcohol misuse

- to provide services of proven effectiveness that enable people to overcome their alcohol misuse problems.

9.14 An effective strategy to tackle alcohol misuse needs the co-operation of all those concerned with alcohol: health and social services, schools, the alcohol industry, law enforcement agencies, Government and the general public. We shall carefully consider the views of all the above to ensure that our strategy provides a coherent and balanced framework for action to tackle alcohol misuse and its consequences. We intend to take this work forward, in partnership with health and industry interests. We expect to publish our strategy after consultation early in the year 2000.

Food safety

9.15 People are now generally well aware of the risks to health which may be carried through the food chain. Communicable diseases like salmonella can cause severe illness and sometimes death. Outbreaks of food-borne diseases largely result from poor standards in the production, preparation or delivery of food. And numbers of reports of food poisoning have been rising. It is therefore important that high standards are set and monitored.

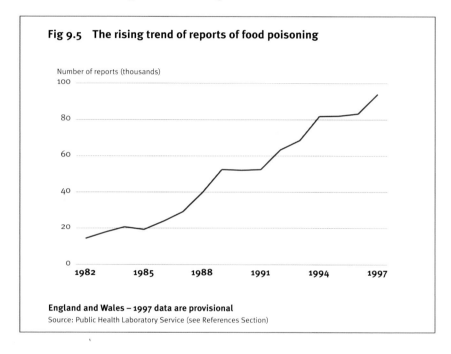

Fig 9.5 The rising trend of reports of food poisoning

Number of reports (thousands)

England and Wales – 1997 data are provisional
Source: Public Health Laboratory Service (see References Section)

'an independent Food Standards Agency, responsible for setting, maintaining and monitoring food standards and safety'

9.16 Last year we published a consultation document setting out in detail the commitment we made in our manifesto to set up an independent Food Standards Agency, responsible for setting, maintaining and, with local authorities, monitoring food standards and safety.

9.17 The Agency will provide independent and authoritative advice to the public on all food safety and standards issues, as well as on a balanced diet, and on the nutritional value of foods, to help people make informed decisions about what they eat. Following consultation on the draft legislation earlier this year, the Food Standards Bill to give effect to these proposals was introduced into Parliament on 10 June.

Water fluoridation

'water fluoridation improves dental health and significantly reduces inequality'

9.18 There are wide variations in dental health across the country. The Acheson Inquiry reinforced the fact that there is strong evidence that water fluoridation improves dental health and significantly reduces inequality in dental health. Children in deprived areas where the water supply is not fluoridated can have up to four times more tooth decay than children in affluent areas, or where water is fluoridated. Responses to the Green Paper were overwhelmingly in support of fluoridation in areas where the level of tooth decay was high.

'the present legislation on fluoridation is not working'

9.19 It is clear that the present legislation on fluoridation is not working. No new schemes have been implemented since 1985. Once a health authority has established that there is strong local support for doing so it may request a water company to fluoridate the water supply. Over 50 health authorities have made such requests to water companies, but to date none has been agreed. The companies are reluctant to take this step when a small but vocal minority are opposed to it. As a result there is deadlock.

'we have commissioned an expert scientific review of fluoride and health'

9.20 We are conscious that the extensive research linking water fluoridation to improved dental health was mostly undertaken a few years ago. So we have commissioned the Centre for Reviews and Dissemination at York University to carry out an up-to-date expert scientific review of fluoride and health. If it confirms that there are benefits to dental health from fluoridation and that there are no significant risks, we intend to introduce a legal obligation on water companies to fluoridate where there is strong local support for doing so. And to ensure that the extent and validity of that public support is beyond all doubt we envisage transferring from health authorities to local authorities the requirement to undertake public consultation on fluoridating the local water supply.

'transferring to local authorities the requirement to undertake public consultation'

Communicable disease

9.21 Communicable disease is one of the main causes of avoidable illness. In the past such diseases as polio, measles, whooping cough and diphtheria were the cause of many deaths in childhood.

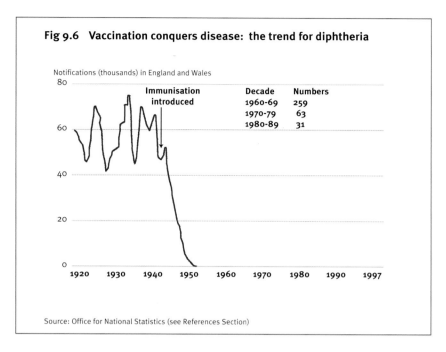

Fig 9.6   Vaccination conquers disease: the trend for diphtheria

Notifications (thousands) in England and Wales

Decade	Numbers
1960-69	259
1970-79	63
1980-89	31

Immunisation introduced

Source: Office for National Statistics (see References Section)

9.22 Now the impact of those diseases in our country has almost completely disappeared as a direct result of the success of the childhood vaccination and immunisation programme. Vaccination programmes have completely eliminated smallpox worldwide. But we cannot afford to be complacent. Notifications of tuberculosis had dropped to a steady 5,000 a year in England and Wales but there has been a recent rise in notifications which must be countered.

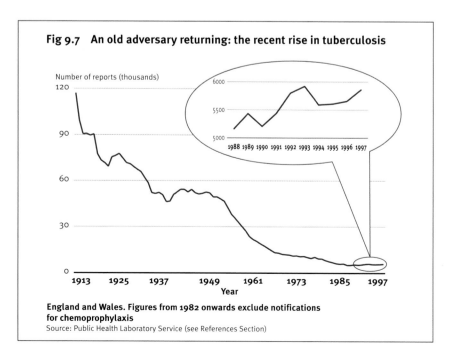

Fig 9.7   An old adversary returning: the recent rise in tuberculosis

Number of reports (thousands)

Year

England and Wales. Figures from 1982 onwards exclude notifications for chemoprophylaxis
Source: Public Health Laboratory Service (see References Section)

9.23 In many cases the organisms which cause disease are evolving in ways which make our traditional defences ineffective. We are beginning to see old diseases return, this time resistant to antibiotics. And at the same time new diseases such as HIV/AIDS are emerging. To combat this threat we have asked the Government's Chief Medical Officer, Professor Liam Donaldson, to develop a strategy for tackling communicable disease to bring major reductions in the amount of illness, disease and death it causes.

The genetics revolution

'By 2003 the Human Genome Project will have mapped all 100,000 genes in the human body'

9.24 As we approach the new millennium we are on the brink of one of the most important scientific achievements in the history of humankind. By 2003, perhaps earlier, the *Human Genome Project* will have mapped all 100,000 genes in the human body. Genes provide a code for the structure and function of our bodies. They also determine our risks and susceptibility to disease. They are made up of strands of DNA – a single sequence of body chemicals, which has been described as "the secret of life". The structure of DNA was discovered by British and US scientists in 1953. Fifty years later the mapping of our entire genetic make-up will have profound implications for health, disease, diagnosis and treatment.

9.25 We already know about many particular genetic disorders which will cause serious disease – for example haemophilia and cystic fibrosis. We know that some diseases can run in families – for example, breast cancer – and geneticists are gradually unravelling the genes which cause them.

9.26 At some time in the future it will be possible to map the genetic code of individuals and understand their risk of developing particular diseases through their whole lifetime. Most diseases are the result of a complex interaction between genes, environment, and lifestyle. So the opportunity will be there to provide an individual with detailed advice on how to reduce any health risks which might otherwise result from his or her genetic make-up.

9.27 This heralds a scientific and technological revolution. When it arrives, we will be ready to use the advances in ways which will enhance the opportunities for better health and prevention of disease, while taking account of the wider social, ethical and economic consequences. Effort will be targeted on those most in need. The new Human Genetics Commission, announced in May this year, will take on this task.

9.28 We will also establish a high level Task Force on Genetics and Disease Prevention which will work to the new Human Genetics Commission.

'a high level Task Force on Genetics and Disease Prevention'

Improving health for black and minority ethnic groups

9.29 In addressing the health of people from black and minority ethnic groups we need a new approach. It is now absolutely clear that some minority ethnic groups carry a higher burden of poor health, premature deaths and long-term disabilities than other groups in the population. We need to address these issues. But simply to tackle them as a list of problems is to fail to recognise the fundamental nature of the change of approach which is required. The report of the Inquiry into the death of black teenager Stephen Lawrence has reinforced our commitment to the root and branch reform we had already begun in the way in which services assess and meet the needs of those from minority ethnic groups. This is equally so not just for health services but for local partnerships and programmes of action aimed at improving the health of local communities. There must be genuine involvement of minority ethnic groups in these endeavours and programmes must be designed through their eyes, not on an assumption of what seems right.

'the death of black teenager Stephen Lawrence has reinforced our commitment to root and branch reform'

9.30 We are determined to tackle racism and racial discrimination wherever it occurs. Since taking office we have already more than doubled the proportion of black and minority ethnic people appointed to the boards of NHS bodies, so that they are more representative of the local people they serve. We have changed the arrangements for deciding on distinction and merit awards for consultants and the number of black and Asian doctors receiving such awards has increased by 50 per cent. We have

'effective action to combat discrimination'

published an action plan *Tackling racial harassment in the NHS* which sets targets for reducing incidents of racial harassment, and we are supporting it through a major public awareness campaign to highlight the impact of such harassment. And in December 1998 we held the first awards ceremony for the NHS Equality Awards, rewarding NHS bodies which have taken clear and effective action to combat discrimination, including on grounds of racial origin.

9.31 Our strategy of targeting prevention, treatment and care of those most in need is particularly relevant to people from black and minority ethnic groups. They include some of the people with the worst health in this country. We need to make sure that our plans for achieving the twin goals of this strategy address the particular needs of these groups.

9.32 At present some people from minority ethnic groups have difficulty getting access to health services – health promotion as well as treatment. And when they fall ill their illnesses are diagnosed later and treatment starts later than for others.

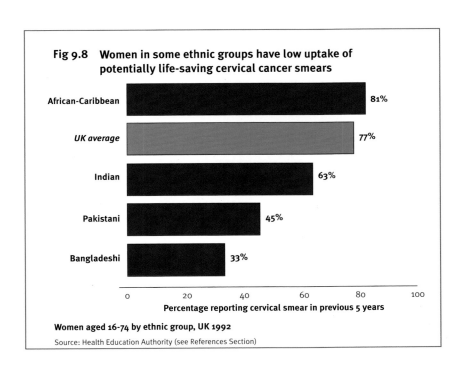

Fig 9.8 Women in some ethnic groups have low uptake of potentially life-saving cervical cancer smears

African-Caribbean — 81%
UK average — 77%
Indian — 63%
Pakistani — 45%
Bangladeshi — 33%

Percentage reporting cervical smear in previous 5 years

Women aged 16-74 by ethnic group, UK 1992

Source: Health Education Authority (see References Section)

9.33 There are also differences in the nature or incidence of illnesses which minority ethnic groups suffer. Some relate to the major killer diseases. For example people born in South Asia are at greater risk from heart disease than most other people in this country, while Afro-Caribbeans have high rates of stroke. Particular diseases such as sickle cell anaemia and thalassaemia occur mainly among specific groups. Taken together, this means not just that health workers need to be especially alert to spot early symptoms of disease among such people; but also that programmes must be tailored in ways which enable people in those groups to reduce their risk from the diseases.

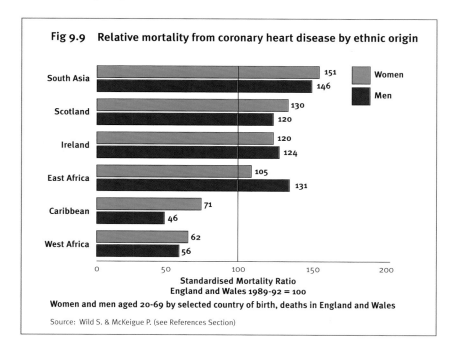

Fig 9.9   Relative mortality from coronary heart disease by ethnic origin

South Asia — Women 151, Men 146
Scotland — Women 130, Men 120
Ireland — Women 120, Men 124
East Africa — Women 105, Men 131
Caribbean — Women 71, Men 46
West Africa — Women 62, Men 56

Standardised Mortality Ratio
England and Wales 1989-92 = 100
Women and men aged 20-69 by selected country of birth, deaths in England and Wales

Source: Wild S. & McKeigue P. (see References Section)

9.34 Communication is sometimes a barrier between minority ethnic patients and health professionals. Certain health authorities have appointed linkworkers and patients' advocates to address this problem. This has helped patients to access and understand health services, particularly when they need specialist help. Patients are better able to discuss their anxieties with linkworkers.

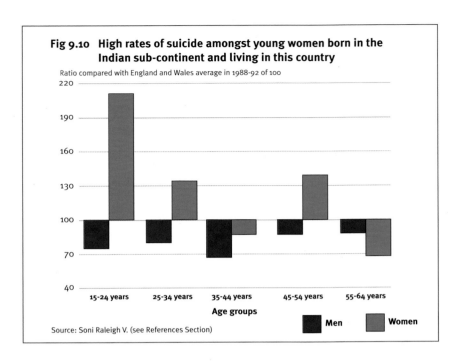

Fig 9.10 **High rates of suicide amongst young women born in the Indian sub-continent and living in this country**

Ratio compared with England and Wales average in 1988-92 of 100

Age groups

■ Men   ■ Women

Source: Soni Raleigh V. (see References Section)

'We must match services to the needs of all people'

9.35 Black and minority ethnic groups have certain well-established health and cultural practices. Failure to recognise, understand and be sensitive to differing cultures has been an area in which services have failed in the past. We must match services to the needs of all people, for example by making ethnic diets available in hospitals; by providing appropriate spiritual care; and enabling those who would prefer to see a female doctor to do so – a measure which would encourage more Asian women, for example, to take up potentially life-saving screening programmes.

9.36 Statutory organisations are working increasingly with individuals, families and communities from black and minority ethnic groups to understand diversity, the different cultural traditions and the various ways in which people from those communities express themselves. For example, health authorities and community organisations are working in mosques, gurdwaras and temples to set up health services including screening services. In this way the local communities have more say in the organisation and delivery of such services.

10 Making it work: progress and partnerships

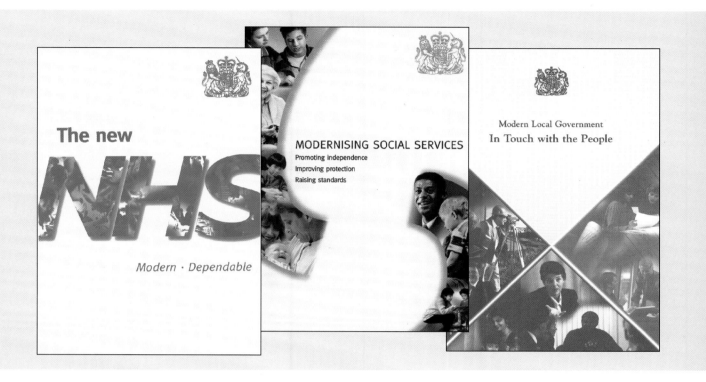

10.1 The goals of this health strategy will be achieved only by a joint effort. That means individuals taking steps to improve their own health, and on new directions and new more effective partnerships formed at local community level between the NHS, local authorities and other agencies.

10.2 Our new approach to better health comprises:

- reorienting local services – including the NHS – to give a high priority to health improvement

- local partnerships for health, where organisations and people work together to improve health overall.

REORIENTING AND EMPOWERING HEALTH SERVICES

'Health authorities have overall responsibility for improving health locally'

10.3 Our determination to modernise the NHS, including ending the wasteful internal market, placing new duties on health authorities, and the creation of primary care groups which are close to patients, is not simply an agenda for improving the reliability and effectiveness of health care services. It is an agenda which will help to improve health overall and to tackle inequality. Health authorities have overall responsibility for improving health locally. Within the health authority the director of public health generally leads this work, accounting for it to the chief executive. In the past public health staff, including the director, had to spend too much time servicing the demands of the internal market. As a result a valuable public health resource was dissipated. The importance of the role of public health was not always clearly reflected through local priorities and too often public health was seen as something which someone else did.

10.4 We are modernising the NHS, and have abolished the internal market. In its place we have introduced a new structure based on partnership working linked to a new duty of co-operation between NHS bodies and local authorities.

10.5 As part of the modernisation process, we have placed a duty on health authorities to draw up health improvement programmes which tackle the health and health care needs of their area. This gives them a key role in improving the health of the local people they serve and we are encouraging them to develop public health expertise throughout their workforce and to apply it across the range of their activities. They must ensure that health problems are tackled and health inequality is addressed. This is reflected in the *National Priorities Guidance* we issued last autumn to health and local authorities, and again in the guidance we have issued for developing local health improvement programmes. NHS Trusts, too, will have a major part to play in the delivery of our health strategy, for example through their contribution to the National Service Frameworks, and in their role as large employers.

10.6 In particular health authorities will:

- identify local health and health care needs

- promote action to achieve demonstrable health improvements and reductions in health inequality

- at local level set the direction within the NHS for delivering service improvements

- provide support to the local health community and encourage opportunities for development

- fulfil their statutory functions in respect of regulating local NHS bodies

- enable, encourage and support the development of local partnerships for health.

New primary care organisations

10.7 We have placed primary care at the heart of our programme to modernise the health service. We are strengthening these services by introducing new primary care groups and the prospect of primary care trusts. These new organisations consist of broadly-based, multi-professional teams including family doctors, nurses, public health professionals, other practitioners and therapists.

10.8 Primary care groups began work in April 1999. Over time we expect them and, when established, primary care trusts, to play a leading role in improving health and cutting inequality, working closely with their local communities. They have strong links with local people and are well placed to do this. In some areas the best primary care teams have already taken on this wider public health role.

10.9 Primary care groups and primary care trusts will take on a range of important new responsibilities which were set out in guidance last December:

- to improve the health of, and address health inequality in, the local community

- to develop primary and community health services by improving the quality of those services, and dealing with poor performance in primary care service providers

- to commission services for their patients from NHS hospital trusts.

10.10 Primary care groups and primary care trusts must continue to ensure that preventive services – some cancer screening, immunisation and vaccination – are available as necessary. They will also continue, for example, to provide help to those wishing to give up smoking or to lose weight.

'we expect primary care groups to forge powerful local partnerships to deliver shared health goals'

10.11 However we expect primary care groups and primary care trusts to go beyond simply the provision of existing preventive services. Over time they too will forge powerful local partnerships with local bodies – schools, employers, housing departments – to deliver shared health goals. They will help shape the health improvement programme and draw up their own plans for implementing it and for hitting the targets in it.

Key features of core roles of health authorities and primary care groups and primary care trusts

Health authorities	Primary care groups and primary care trusts
• enabling	• doing
• gaining multi-sector commitment and co-ordination	• forging local partnerships
• setting strategy (jointly with others)	• planning action
• prioritising and investing in public health programmes	• resourcing action plans
• developing public health organisational and people capability	• building workforce capacity and public health infrastructure
• monitoring progress	• meeting objectives

LOCAL PARTNERSHIPS:

Leading health improvement

10.12 Tackling poor health and health inequality needs the NHS and local government to take joint responsibility. There are several parts of the country where NHS bodies, local authorities and others already work well together. But there are others where they work less well.

10.13 Successful partnership working is built on organisations moving together to address common goals; on developing in their staff the skills necessary to work in an entirely new way – across boundaries, in multi-disciplinary teams, and in a culture in which learning and good practice are shared. It also means:

'a culture in which learning and good practice are shared'

- clarifying the common purpose of the partnership

- recognising and resolving potential areas of conflict

- agreeing a shared approach to partnership

- strong leadership based on a clear vision and drive, with well-developed influencing and networking skills

- continuously adapting to reflect the lessons learned from experience

- promoting awareness and understanding of partner organisations through joint training programmes and incentives to reward effective working across organisational boundaries.

10.14 Through the Health Act 1999 we have extended the existing duty of partnership between health authorities and local authorities to NHS Trusts and primary care trusts (when established), reflecting the need for partnership in service commissioning and delivery as well as strategic planning. All this is underpinned by new financial flexibilities, including powers to operate pooled budgets. This will create the opportunity for the new style of partnership we want to promote.

Effective planning for health

10.15 Local health improvement programmes will reflect these new partnerships. They will be genuinely joint enterprises with local authorities and others. The role of local authorities in improving health locally will be clearly defined and reflected in their priorities and any community plans. Health improvement programmes will also show how the National Service Frameworks will be implemented at local level. So they will be effective vehicles for making a major and sustained impact on the health problems of every locality in the country. As well as looking at the overall health of the local population, they will also focus action on people who are socially excluded and need the most support.

10.16 The main responsibility for developing health improvement programmes rests with the health authority, drawing on the contributions of other NHS bodies, local authorities and others including local businesses, voluntary bodies, community groups and individuals. Universities and those responsible for the education and training of professional staff will also play a part.

'Local authorities will be key contributors to the health improvement programme'

10.17 Local authorities are at the centre of local public service provision. They will be key contributors to the health improvement programme through the best value initiative and any community plans which they develop in partnership with other local bodies to promote the economic, social and environmental well-being of their communities.

Health improvement programmes

10.18 Health improvement programmes will:

- give a clear description of how the national aims, contracts and targets will be tackled locally

- set out a range of locally-determined priorities and targets with particular emphasis on addressing areas of major health inequality

- specify agreed programmes of action to address these national and local health improvement priorities

- show that the action proposed is based on evidence of what is known to work (from research and best practice reports)

- show what measures of local progress will be used (including those required for national monitoring purposes)

- indicate which local organisations have been involved in drawing up the plan, what their contribution will be and how they will be held to account for delivering it

- ensure that the plan is easy to understand and accessible to the public

- also be a vehicle for setting strategies for the shaping of local health services.

10.19 Health improvement programmes are so central to achieving our aims that we want to recognise the success of those health authority areas which, working through NHS and local authority partners, are making a real difference in improving health and tackling health inequality locally. So we are setting up a *Health Improvement Programme Performance Scheme.* The Scheme will reward health authorities which have made the best progress in meeting their targets and objectives. In particular, it will recognise those health communities making progress from a low base, tackling entrenched problems of ill-health, deprivation and poor or fragmented services. In the first year we are investing at least an additional £10 million to drive forward implementation of the *National Service Framework on Coronary Heart Disease.*

'a Health Improvement Programme Performance Scheme will recognise health communities making progress from a low base, tackling entrenched problems of ill-health, deprivation and poor or fragmented services'

10.20 We will also:

- invite NHS organisations to apply for beacon status where they have examples of good practice. The first 259 NHS Beacons were announced in May including 24 focused specifically on health improvement

- require health authorities to make available on the Internet an annual core health statement. These statements, drawn from local health improvement programmes, will enable experts from around the world to offer advice on the effectiveness of the approach taken.

Building local capability: regenerating health in communities

'Real change can come only from the local community itself by harnessing the energy, skills and commitment of local people'

10.21 There is increasing evidence, including from the World Health Organisation, that having strong social networks benefits health. When people are involved in making the decisions which affect their lives their self-esteem and self-confidence rise, in turn improving their health and well-being. And, of course, many local people, including local workers such as health visitors, have a good understanding of the community's main health problems and of priorities for action.

10.22 For most people these issues come together at the neighbourhood level. We will encourage local people to make their neighbourhoods healthier, for example by identifying and sharing good practice. Real change can come only from the local community itself by harnessing the energy, skills and commitment of local people in setting clear objectives for change and forming new partnerships for action. Sometimes certain individuals – "social entrepreneurs" – are particularly effective in focusing community action to secure change.

Health action zones

10.23 *Health action zones* are leading the way in breaking down organisational barriers. They are using imaginative new ways of providing services which cross boundaries between organisations. We established eleven health action zones from April 1998, and a further 15 started in April this year in some of the most deprived parts of the country. They cover both urban and rural areas.

Healthy living centres

10.24 The development of *healthy living centres* will help people struggling with health problems which may not need medical treatment. Healthy living centres will provide a way in which they can find help and support within their local community. Healthy living centres:

- will promote good health in its broadest sense

- may include a range of facilities, including health screening facilities, dietary advice, smoking cessation, employment, training and skills schemes, parenting classes, exercise classes and child care

- will involve the local community in the planning of the projects.

10.25 They will be funded throughout the UK with £300 million of Lottery money. The first Lottery applications for healthy living centre funding are likely to be agreed this autumn.

10.26 We recognise that there is a great deal of expertise within local communities, and in non-Governmental organisations. At local level we will encourage health authorities, local communities, primary care groups and primary care trusts to make use of non-Governmental organisations in delivering programmes. At a national level we will establish a National Forum of Non-Governmental Public Health Organisations to offer expertise and advice.

'there is a great deal of expertise within local communities, and in non-Governmental organisations'

11 Making it work: standards and success

11.1 People, local communities through key organisations and the Government working together to improve the health of our nation will bring about a significant change in our overall health. But for that partnership to work, the quality of public health practice has to be of the highest possible standard. And in order to know how far and how quickly our drive for improved health is working, we have to be able to measure progress. So our programme for better health has to have both sensible standards and observable measures of success.

'the quality of public health practice is mixed'

Standards

11.2 In some local areas the quality of public health practice is excellent but across the country as a whole the picture is mixed. Many organisations want to do much more to improve the health of the populations they serve. Yet they are often unclear about what they should expect from the programmes they create or from the staff they employ to deliver public health goals.

11.3 Setting standards and measuring progress is now an integral part of the planning and delivery of services to patients in primary care and hospitals within the new NHS.

11.4 Standard setting for public health is not nearly so straightforward. Public heath is multi-disciplinary and multi-agency so standards need to be flexible enough to apply in different organisations and to staff with different backgrounds and training. In addition we do not yet have enough robust evidence in many fields of health on which to base standards. But that does not mean that standards do not have to be set. They do.

11.5 To help address these issues the Government has decided to establish a Health Development Agency. The Agency will ensure that organisations and individual practitioners base their work on the highest standards and over time raise the quality of the public health function in England.

'the Government has decided to establish a Health Development Agency'

11.6 In advising and supporting the Secretary of State for Health the new Agency's key functions will include:

- maintaining an up-to-date map of the evidence base for public health and health improvement

- commissioning such research and evaluation as is necessary to support and strengthen the evidence base in areas where action programmes are required to improve health and tackle inequality, within an agreed framework governed by the Secretary of State's overall research strategy for health

- in the light of the evidence, advising on the setting of standards for public health and health promotion practice, and on the implementation of those standards by a range of organisations at national and local level

- in particular, providing advice on targeting health promotion most effectively on the worst off and narrowing the health gap

- through regular bulletins, guidance and advice, disseminating information on effectiveness and good practice in an authoritative, timely and effective manner to those working in the public health/health promotion field

'advising on the setting of standards for public health and health promotion practice'

- commissioning and carrying out evidence-based national health promotion programmes and campaigns which are integrated with the Department of Health's overall communications strategy and linked with regional and local activity

- advising on the capacity and capability of the public health workforce to deliver Ministers' strategy in these areas to the agreed standards, and on the education and training needs of the workforce, ensuring throughout that such advice is informed by research evidence and the appropriate quality standards.

Our Healthier Nation in Practice

To increase people's access to information about what is happening on the ground, especially on imaginative, innovative and successful ideas, we are also setting up a database of practice – *Our Healthier Nation in Practice* – as part of the *Our Healthier Nation* internet site on *www.ohn.gov.uk*. This will allow people to search the database for information and learning from a wide range of initiatives. The database will provide a direct contact name and number to encourage sharing of the detailed experience available.

11.7 The Agency will be a statutory body, with the status of a Special Health Authority. It will be established within existing public health resources. The resources of the Health Education Authority will be used to form the core of the new Agency and, consequently, subject to Parliamentary approval, the new Agency will supersede the Health Education Authority. The newly-appointed Chair of the Authority – and its new Board of Non-Executive Directors – will be invited to become the first Chair and Non-Executive Directors of the Agency. The intention is for the Agency to come into being on 1 January next year, subject to passage of necessary legislation through Parliament. The Agency will work closely with the Department of Health including the NHS Executive and its Regional Offices, Government Offices for the Regions, Regional Development Agencies, local authorities and other key players in the field, including the proposed Food Standards Agency.

EDUCATION AND TRAINING FOR HEALTH

11.8 We need to make sure that the public health workforce is skilled, staffed and resourced to deal with the major task of delivering our health strategy.

11.9 Medically-qualified public health staff have played a vital role in the development of the public health movement from the first Medical Officers of Health in Victorian England to the Directors of Public Health today. They must continue to do so in the future but as part of a modern public health workforce made up of people from a wide range of professional backgrounds.

> **We must ensure that all these diverse groups of professional staff can as necessary:**
>
> • manage strategic change
>
> • act as leaders and champions of public health
>
> • work in partnership with other agencies and individuals
>
> • develop communities with a focus on health
>
> • be familiar with public health concepts and use where appropriate evidence in guiding their work
>
> • apply their professional skills and knowledge to play a part in securing the aims set out in this White Paper.

'Those without medical backgrounds have had to put together "do it yourself" careers in public health'

11.10 The challenge of achieving these goals is enormous but the potential benefit of ensuring that a diverse grouping of individual professionals becomes a true public health workforce is huge.

11.11 There are a number of barriers to achieving this. First is the absence of a true multi-disciplinary basis to public health practice. In the past the rhetoric has been strong but it has not always been followed through into practice. Those without medical backgrounds have had to put together "do it yourself" careers in public health. Even then they have often had relatively low status and recognition for their skills and expertise. Secondly, because public health has seemed a less pressing priority than financial and workload imperatives, many managers in the NHS have spent little of their skill and energy on implementing health strategy. Thirdly, there has been insufficient interdisciplinary working across organisational boundaries.

'to unlock the potential of the entire public health workforce'

11.12 We intend to address these traditional deficits: to unlock the potential of the entire public health workforce. So we will produce a *Public Health Workforce National Development Plan*. In doing so we will work particularly with the professional bodies responsible for training and education of this diverse range of professional groups.

11.13 To help with the plan we will also rapidly complete a *Public Health Skills Audit* to determine the current baseline of capacity and capability to deliver our goals through a skilled workforce. We will then expect local health organisations to decide whether they have the right mix of skills to prepare themselves for the shift to the new population- and health-focused agenda of the 21st Century.

Nurses and public health

11.14 Nurses, midwives and health visitors play a crucial part in promoting health and preventing illness. People have close contact with them at key points in their lives – in infancy, during adolescence, pregnancy and childbirth, and in sickness and old age – creating significant opportunities for health promoting interventions.

11.15 We are developing a strategy for nursing, midwifery and health visiting which will help strengthen the public health aspects of their roles. While recognising the potential of all nurses to contribute to public health it will include a focus on the roles of health visitors, school nurses, infection control and occupational health nurses as public health practitioners.

Health visitors as public health practitioners

'modernising the role of health visitors'

11.16 We are modernising the role of health visitors to enable them to respond effectively to the challenge of the Government's new policies. So we are encouraging them to develop a family-centred public health role, working with individuals, families and communities to improve health and tackle health inequality.

11.17 As a result of this modern role:

- parents will receive improved support including parenting education, health advice and information

- individuals and families will be able to have a tailored family health plan agreed in partnership with the health visitor to address their parenting and health needs

- the health needs of families and communities will be met by a team led by a health visitor including nurses, nursery nurses, and community workers

- health visitors will initiate and develop programmes for outreach, based on the experience of organisations such as *Homestart, New pin* and 'community mothers', where local parents use their experience to support others

- neighbourhoods or special groups such as homeless people within a practice or primary care group will have their health needs identified by health visitors, who will lead public health practice and agree local health plans

- local communities will be helped to identify and address their own health needs, for example accident prevention for older people.

'health visitors will lead public health practice and agree local health plans'

11.18 A team led by the health visitor will provide a range of health improvement activities including:

- child health programmes

- parenting support and education including support to *Sure Start*, parenting groups and home visits

- developing support networks in communities, for example tackling social isolation in older people

- support and advice for breastfeeding mothers and women at risk of post-natal depression

- health promotion programmes to target cancer, coronary heart disease and stroke, accidents and mental health

- advice on family relationships and support to vulnerable children and their families.

School nurses as public health practitioners

'The school nursing team will provide a range of health improvement activities'

11.19 School nurses are ideally placed to help children, young people and their parents find the support and services they need. The potential to develop school nurses is a growing element within the *Healthy Schools* programme and their role is being increasingly considered within other Government initiatives, such as tackling teenage pregnancy. Responses to the Home Office document *Supporting Families* have highlighted the importance of the work of school nurses with families.

11.20 School nurses can provide advice and help in areas such as personal relationships, managing stress and risk-taking behaviours. They can complement primary care services by providing a safety-net for children, particularly the most disadvantaged, who may not have had a full child health service before starting school. Their role needs to be developed and supported to enable them to:

- lead teams

- assess the health needs of individuals and school communities and agree individual and school health plans

- develop multi-disciplinary partnerships with teachers, general practitioners, health visitors and child and adolescent mental health professionals to deliver agreed health plans.

11.21 The school nursing team will provide a range of health improvement activities including:

- immunisation and vaccination programmes

- support and advice to teachers and other school staff on a range of child health issues

- support to children with medical needs

- support and counselling to promote positive mental health in young people

- personal health and social education programmes and citizenship training

- identification of social care needs, including the need for protection from abuse

- providing advice on relationships and sex education by building on their clinical experience and pastoral role

- aiding liaison between, for example, schools, primary care groups, and special services in meeting the health and social care needs of children

- contribute to the identification of children's special educational needs

- working with parents and young people alongside health visitors to promote parenting.

Midwives

11.22 Support for expectant mothers and families with very young children was identified as a high priority by the Acheson Inquiry. Midwives are uniquely placed to improve health and tackle inequality through the innovative services they provide to women and their babies at home and in hospital.

11.23 Midwives can:

- target vulnerable groups through, for example, pregnancy clubs for young single mothers or link workers for black and minority ethnic groups

- provide preconception counselling for prospective parents, targeting smoking cessation, alcohol intake and diet to reduce the risk of low birthweight and premature babies

'Midwives are uniquely placed to improve health and tackle inequality through services to women and their babies'

- work with health visitors and others on post-natal depression, breastfeeding and best practice to avoid Sudden Infant Death Syndrome (cot deaths).

Occupational health nurses

11.24 We are developing the public health role of occupational health nurses and communicable disease control nurses to enable them to use population approaches to assess and manage health needs. Occupational health nurses will be an important source of support for a range of action to improve health at work.

Specialists in public health

'creating the post of Specialist in Public Health of equivalent status to medically qualified Consultants'

11.25 We want to develop future cadres of Consultants in Public Health Medicine in a way which recognises the multi-disciplinary basis of public health practice and removes the glass ceiling which limits their career paths at present. Thus, within the NHS we are creating the post of Specialist in Public Health which will be of equivalent status in independent practice to medically qualified Consultants in Public Health Medicine and allow them to become Directors of Public Health. And their expertise would apply to other public sector bodies as well as the NHS.

Medical care epidemiologists

11.26 Public health is not just about the wider aspects of population health. For those with chronic and longstanding conditions, improving the outcome of care can mean reducing disabling complications and enhancing quality of life. Specialist skills are necessary in developing and using outcome measures at local level, in ensuring that information systems capture data and in evaluating clinical interventions and diagnostic tests. NHS Trusts and primary care groups will address these issues in different ways but we will be encouraging them to look at the results of a pilot scheme in the Northern and Yorkshire Region in which Medical Care Epidemiologists have been employed by NHS Trusts.

INFORMATION FOR HEALTH

11.27 We need a clearer national picture of health and health inequality so that we can track changes over time. Many agencies are involved in collecting and using information about health and disease in the population. Yet in some cases information may not be available, or may be unreliable.

11.28 At local level data may be even patchier. Data derived from national health surveys, for example, although offering an excellent national picture will often not be enough to provide the necessary level of information at a more local level.

11.29 We will be carrying out a *Review of National Sources of Public Health Information* to see where they need to be strengthened to increase our ability to assess health and track progress in achieving the goals of this White Paper.

11.30 In order to strengthen the availability and use of information about health at local level we will ensure that there is a *Public Health Observatory* in each NHS region of the country. These observatories will be closely linked with universities to help bring an academic rigour to their work. Their main tasks will be to support local bodies by:

- monitoring health and disease trends and highlighting areas for action

- identifying gaps in health information

- advising on methods for health and health inequality impact assessments

- drawing together information from different sources in new ways to improve health

- carrying out projects to highlight particular health issues

- evaluating progress by local agencies in improving health and cutting inequality

'we will ensure that there is a Public Health Observatory in each NHS region of the country'

LIVERPOOL PUBLIC HEALTH OBSERVATORY

Examples of topics covered since 1990 include

- planned parenthood

- family planning, abortion and fertility

- coronary heart disease and stroke

- drug misuse and drug misuse services

- alcohol abuse; needs assessment and services review

- deafness

- asthma and environmental pollution

- environmental causes of death and disability

- tuberculosis and poverty

- cystic fibrosis and deprivation

- health impact assessment of the Merseyside Integrated Transport Strategy.

- looking ahead to give early warning of future public health problems.

11.31 Public health observatories will work closely with NHS bodies, local authorities, NHS Executive Regional Offices, the Government Offices for the Regions and Regional Development Agencies as well as the new Health Development Agency. They will be linked together to form a national network of knowledge, information and surveillance in public health and will be a major new resource for local bodies working in public health.

11.32 The Liverpool Public Health Observatory was established in 1990, and provides some of the key elements which will be necessary in establishing the new network of observatories.

11.33 We will strengthen the information base on chronic diseases in the population by establishing a series of *Disease Registers* in different parts of the country. These registers will enable us to know, for example, how many people in a population are suffering from coronary heart disease, stroke, diabetes, asthma, high blood pressure. They will act as a base for investigation into disease causes, for evaluating new ways of delivering services as well as tracking changes in disease occurrence over time. These registers will draw on the work which we have already put in train through our *Information for Health* programme, and will complement the existing registers for cancer.

11.34 We will also use in a more systematic way the annual reports by Directors of Public Health, which are an important source of information on the main health problems and issues. We will ensure that they are used as a basis for the formulation of health improvement programmes and are fully relevant to local authorities as well as health authorities. We will ensure that they meet a common set of standards.

RESEARCH

11.35 Research plays a major role in helping us understand better the causes of ill-health, including the different ways our lifestyle and environment affect our health and our children's health. Public health research is also important in establishing the effectiveness of health programmes but we need to widen the scope of the methods used beyond the randomised controlled trial. In the past it has been the gold standard for research but it is no longer applicable to all the kinds of research questions which need to be answered.

11.36   We are carefully mapping all available research and will draw on it to develop a *Research and Development Strategy for Public Health*. In doing this we will make sure that the results of research are easily accessible to those who need to use them, that the programmes of work tackle our priority areas, that methods are appropriate and innovative and that there is a skilled research and development workforce in place.

11.37   The NHS spends around £420 million annually on research. Much of this investment covers the four priority areas for this health strategy – cancer, coronary heart disease and stroke, accidents and mental health. The Central Research and Development Committee for the NHS has established review groups in each of the four priority areas. These groups will report in the autumn, and recommend any necessary realignment of this research and development spending to ensure the most effective contribution to *Our Healthier Nation*.

11.38   Given the importance of a sound evidence base to underpin public health there needs also to be a strong and high-quality academic base to support both research and teaching. Unfortunately at present academic public health is not as rigorous as we would like to see it. Younger people are not opting for careers in the discipline and senior academic posts are becoming more difficult to fill. We want to create a climate in which academic excellence can flourish. So we are setting up a *Fast Track Development Programme* for young public health academics who will be the catalyst for the transformation we are seeking to achieve. As a first step we are setting up a pilot project in which research fellowships are jointly created between the Medical Research Council and the NHS Research and Development Directorate linked to a new initiative, *The Health of the Public*.

'We want to create a climate in which academic excellence can flourish'

'*We are creating a Public Health Development Fund*'

INVESTING FOR PROGRESS

11.39 We are creating a *Public Health Development Fund* as part of the Modernisation Fund for Health. It will be worth at least £96 million over three years. It will provide seed corn for new approaches in public health, to help and encourage the development of innovative ideas and to help tackle health inequality. The Fund will principally support action to save lives within the priority areas set out in this White Paper.

11.40 Spending plans for the first year, amounting to £25 million, are already well advanced and cover a range of national, regional and local initiatives. The Fund will focus on four distinctive, though complementary, programmes, each designed to underpin the strategic framework in this White Paper. The first (£9 million in 1999/00) is directed primarily to the priority areas of cancer, coronary heart disease and stroke, accidents and mental health, but includes also work on infant feeding and the Health Visiting and School Nursing Innovation Fund. The second programme (£3.5 million) will help to develop the range of healthy settings. The third (£3.5 million) will fund key aspects of our *Healthy Citizens* programme that are not already being resourced in other ways. And the fourth (£9 million) will support the public health strategy as a whole in areas such as health impact assessment, the development of public health observatories and the improvement of infection control. This programme includes £4 million to be spent at regional level on a range of activities that, among other things, will help to develop the public health function.

'*we have decided to set interim milestones in each of the four priority areas*'

Success

11.41 We are setting out an ambitious programme to achieve our goals and targets for a long-term sustained improvement in health. They will take many years to deliver fully; and we need to be able to check our progress along the way. So we have decided to set interim milestones in each of the four priority areas for 2005. These milestones will tell us if we are on course to achieve our targets for the year 2010.

11.42 Our assessment of progress will cover:

- the targets themselves – reduction in mortality rates in our four priority areas of cancer, coronary heart disease and stroke, accidents and mental health

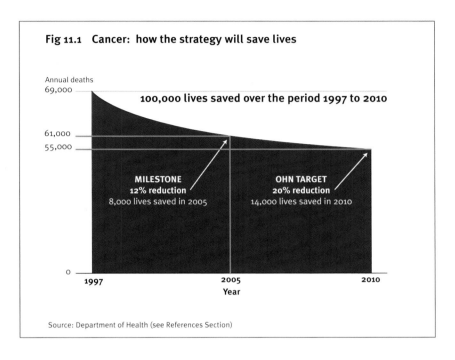

Fig 11.1 Cancer: how the strategy will save lives

Annual deaths

100,000 lives saved over the period 1997 to 2010

MILESTONE
12% reduction
8,000 lives saved in 2005

OHN TARGET
20% reduction
14,000 lives saved in 2010

Year

Source: Department of Health (see References Section)

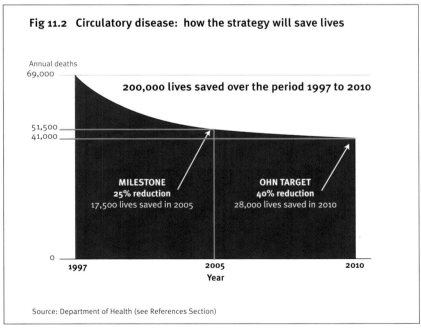

Fig 11.2 Circulatory disease: how the strategy will save lives

Annual deaths

200,000 lives saved over the period 1997 to 2010

MILESTONE
25% reduction
17,500 lives saved in 2005

OHN TARGET
40% reduction
28,000 lives saved in 2010

Year

Source: Department of Health (see References Section)

- improvements in the risk factors which have a direct bearing on our four targets

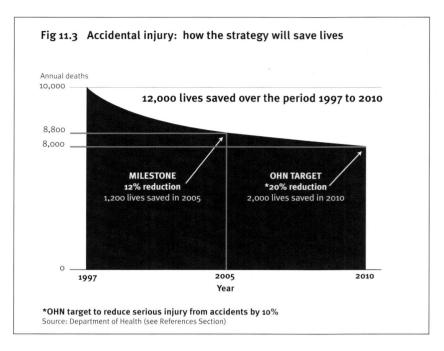

Fig 11.3   Accidental injury: how the strategy will save lives

Annual deaths

12,000 lives saved over the period 1997 to 2010

MILESTONE
12% reduction
1,200 lives saved in 2005

OHN TARGET
***20% reduction**
2,000 lives saved in 2010

Year

*OHN target to reduce serious injury from accidents by 10%
Source: Department of Health (see References Section)

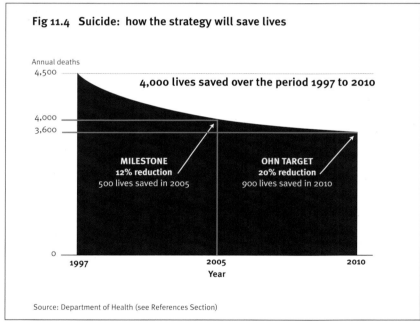

Fig 11.4   Suicide: how the strategy will save lives

Annual deaths

4,000 lives saved over the period 1997 to 2010

MILESTONE
12% reduction
500 lives saved in 2005

OHN TARGET
20% reduction
900 lives saved in 2010

Year

Source: Department of Health (see References Section)

- movement in underlying factors which reflect social, environmental and economic change which the evidence shows to have an influence on health and inequality

- effectiveness of programmes – as part of assessing progress we need to know that action of the right kind is in place, supported by the development of capacity and capability in public health. We will monitor these aspects of progress through a range of mechanisms including health improvement programmes, local authorities' community plans and *Best Value* and the national service frameworks.

11.43 We shall support this process by publishing a Technical Supplement to this White Paper setting out the scientific basis for target setting and the indicators available for the assessment of progress across the whole range of influences on health – environmental and behavioural risk factors, as well as health outcomes.

11.44 To complement our continuous monitoring, every three years we will review and publish changes at national level to:

• expectation of life

• healthy life expectancy

• health inequality

Local targets for improving health

11.45 Much of the action that we are putting in place will be delivered at the level of local communities. We expect health authorities and their partner local authorities as well as other local agencies to set out in their health improvement programme how they plan to achieve the national priorities through targets at local level. Health improvement programmes will be required to include additional local targets to address particular local priorities and to cut health inequality.

Managing performance

11.46 We want the achievement of results in delivering *Saving lives: Our Healthier Nation* to matter as much to local agencies as hitting the targets in the other important programmes they deliver. A health organisation should take as much pride in reaching the targets set out here as in achieving its targets on waiting lists and times. The goals in this White Paper must be as rigorously pursued by performance managers as any other targets.

'We will hold NHS bodies to account through the new NHS performance assessment framework'

*'the new rigour and
drive we are bringing
to public health'*

*'We shall ensure that
public health is
subject to concerted
development and
performance
management'*

11.47   We will hold NHS bodies to account through the new NHS performance assessment framework. The NHS Executive Regional Offices will ensure that they set realistic but demanding targets for local achievement, and will monitor their performance. Where appropriate they will "benchmark" a body's objectives by comparing them with the plans of other bodies in broadly similar circumstances. A parallel performance assessment process applies to social services authorities, while local government overall is subject to the *Best Value* regime. External auditors will provide a rigorous check on the information provided by authorities in local performance plans, and on the management systems that underpin them. There will also be an objective and independent process of regular inspection for all local services.

11.48   To strengthen accountability the Audit Commission is developing ways of auditing areas of joint working between these agencies at local level, using its experience of carrying out local value for money studies.

CONCLUSION

11.49   This White Paper sets out our health strategy for England: the goals, the targets, and how we propose to reach them. Success will be built on the new rigour and drive we are bringing to public health. We expect everyone to play their part in making this strategy deliver its full potential. We shall ensure that public health is subject to the same concerted development and performance management as every other area of Government policy, so that we can secure real and rapid progress. We all stand to gain. This strategy will give us all longer lives, healthier lives, and make ours a fairer country.

Appendix 1

A National Contract on Cancer	People can:	Local Players and Communities can:	Government and National Players can:
Social & Economic	Take opportunities to better their lives and their families' lives through education, training and employment Participate in social networks and provide social support to others to reduce stress, and to give them help to give up smoking	Tackle social exclusion in the community to make it easier for people to make healthy decisions Work with deprived communities and with businesses to ensure a more varied and affordable choice of food (including fruit and vegetables)	Increase the tax on cigarettes by 5 per cent in real terms each year End advertising and promotion of cigarettes Prohibit sale of cigarettes to youngsters and ensure enforcement Seek to ensure cheaper supplies of fruit and vegetables Tackle joblessness, social exclusion, low educational standards and other factors which make it harder to live a healthier life
Environmental	Protect others from secondhand smoke and children from sunburn	Through local employers, make smoke-free environments the norm, with adequate separate provision for smokers and availability of smoke extractors where possible Tackle radon in the home (e.g. through direct advice from local authorities to affected householders)	Encourage employers and others to provide a smoke-free environment for non-smokers Encourage local action to tackle radon in the home and to eliminate risk factors in the workplace (e.g. enforcing regulations on asbestos and encouraging provision of non-smoking areas) and the environment (e.g. air pollutants) Continue to press for international action to restore the ozone layer

A National Contract on Cancer	People can:	Local Players and Communities can:	Government and National Players can:
Personal behaviour	Stop smoking, increase consumption of fruit, vegetables, and dietary fibre each day, avoid high consumption of red and processed meat, keep physically active, maintain a healthy body weight that does not increase during adult life Cover up in the sun Practise safer sex Follow Sensible Drinking advice	Encourage the development of healthy workplaces and healthy schools Target health information on groups and areas where people are most at risk	Develop healthy living centres Fund health education campaigns to provide reliable and objective information on the health risks of smoking, poor diet and too much sun Encourage research into ways to modify high risk behaviours (e.g. low consumption of fruit and vegetables)
Services	Attend cancer screenings when invited (i.e. for breast and cervical screening in women) Seek advice promptly if they notice danger signs Participate in managing their own illness and treatment	Provide effective help in stopping smoking to people who want to stop especially for disadvantaged groups Work with voluntary organisations to provide clear and consistent messages about early detection and uptake of screening Ensure that vulnerable groups have equitable access to screening services Ensure rapid specialist treatment for cancers when they are diagnosed	Encourage doctors, dentists, nurses and other health professionals to give advice on prevention Ensure smokers have access to high-quality smoking cessation services, particularly in health action zones Ensure that healthy schools work with pupils and parents to improve health Maintain effective, appropriate and high quality existing cancer screening programmes and consider possible extensions of these Ensure all patients with suspected cancer are seen by a specialist within 2 weeks of urgent referral by a GP Ensure equal access to high quality treatment and care, through implementation of the expert report on the organisation and management of NHS cancer services

A National Contract on Coronary Heart Disease and Stroke	People can:	Local Players and Communities can:	Government and National Players can:
Social & Economic	Take opportunities to better their lives and their families' lives, through education, training and employment Cycle or walk to work	Tackle social exclusion in the community which makes it harder to have a healthier lifestyle Provide incentives to employees to cycle or walk to work, or leave their cars at home	Continue to make smoking cost more through taxation Tackle joblessness, social exclusion, low educational standards and other factors which make it harder to live a healthier life
Environmental	Protect others from secondhand smoke	Through local employers and others, provide a smoke-free environment for non-smokers Through employers and staff, work in partnership to reduce stress at work Implement the Integrated Transport Policy – *A New Deal for Transport: Better for Everyone* – including a national cycling strategy and measures to make walking more attractive Provide safe cycling and walking routes	Encourage employers and others to provide a smoke-free environment for non-smokers

A National Contract on Coronary Heart Disease and Stroke	People can:	Local Players and Communities can:	Government and National Players can:
Personal behaviour	Stop smoking or cut down, watch what they eat and take regular physical activity Manage their blood pressure if they are at risk of or suffering from circulatory disease	of healthy schools and healthy workplaces Target information about a healthy life on groups and areas where people are most at risk Enforce the ban on illegal sale of cigarettes to underage smokers	Control advertising and promotion of cigarettes Develop healthy living centres Ensure access to and availability of a wide range of foods for a healthy diet Provide sound information on the health risks of smoking, poor diet and lack of physical activity Encourage the development
Services	Learn how to recognise a heart attack and what to do, including resuscitation skills Have their blood pressure checked regularly Take medicine as it is prescribed	Provide help to people who want to stop smoking Reduce waiting times for coronary artery surgery and angioplasty Aim to reduce the incidence of second strokes Improve access to a variety of affordable food in deprived areas Support those suffering from coronary heart disease and stroke, and their carers Provide facilities for physical activity and reliable transport to help people get to them Identify those at high risk of coronary heart disease and stroke and provide high quality services Implement the National Service Frameworks	Encourage doctors and nurses and other health professionals to give advice on healthier living, and deliver effective and efficient services Develop National Service Frameworks and work towards their implementation

A National Contract on Accidents	People can:	Local Players and Communities can:	Government and National Players can:
Social & Economic	Take opportunities to improve their education, training and employment	Monitor care homes for older people

Promote safety practices at work

Tackle social exclusion (*New Deal*, urban regeneration)

Work within health improvement programmes on local partnership to improve local accident prevention initiatives, e.g. better identification of highest risks/priorities/targets

Promote safety measures to community groups

Raise public awareness of risks | Develop *New Deal for Communities*

Remove obstacles to partnership

Promote parental education *(Sure Start)*

Improve provision of consistent monitoring data

Co-ordinate Government strategy on accident prevention |
| Environmental | Install, check and maintain smoke alarms

Maintain household appliances to reduce accidents in the home

Wear seatbelts on car journeys

Drive safely and within speed limits

Ensure that they play an effective role in workplace safety procedures | Install smoke alarms in local and health authority properties

Encourage private sector safety checks on appliances

Develop traffic calming and other measures for local safety schemes as part of local transport plans

Give greater priority to walking and cycling in local transport plans

Adopt school travel and green transport plans

Promote/maintain home safety checks for older people

Develop safe play areas

Maintain highways, pavements and playgrounds

Identify/safeguard potentially hazardous sites (rivers, railways, dumps etc)

Undertake community safety audits/risk assessment

Ensure well-developed emergency planning | Ensure safety standards in new buildings

Continue work on improving product standards

Monitor standards for sports facilities and equipment

Monitor water safety co-ordination at national level

Promote *Design for Safety*

Monitor vehicle safety standards

Support for pilot schemes and voluntary bodies (e.g. Child Safety Week)

Implement EC regulations on accident prevention

Develop road safety strategy |

A National Contract on Accidents	People can:	Local Players and Communities can:	Government and National Players can:
Personal behaviour	Avoid drinking and driving

Ensure that cyclists, especially children and young people, wear cycle helmets

Undertake effective training to improve road safety skills

Ensure that children and young people take up cycle/pedestrian training

Take up physically active lifestyles (to improve bone density and prevent osteoporotic fractures)

Ensure a healthy diet (with sufficient calcium and vitamin D intake for bone health) | Conduct local campaigns (LEAs) on accidental injury prevention

Ensure more effective enforcement – fire, police, trading standards

Put measures in place on prevention (e.g. stairgates, car seats) and rehabilitation (e.g. aids for older people)

Ensure effective provision/loans of safety equipment to target groups

Develop private sector promoting safety culture for occupational road use

Promote swimming training | Provide education/publicity on drink-drive

Provide education/publicity on speed management

Promote accident prevention through schools programmes (Healthy Schools Award)

Promote *Safer Routes to School*

Set up Youth Networks, playgroup associations

Target health action zones/education action zones/SRB/*New Deal for Communities* |
| Services | Have regular eye tests

Learn basic resuscitation/emergency skills | Provide pedestrian training for children

Continue reviews of medication, eyesight in older people (over 75 check)

Promote safety awareness, with risk assessment of fallers, on discharge from hospital

Promote local initiatives on physical activity in older people

Promote cycle proficiency schemes

Promote family support – accident awareness, parenting skills

Take part in *Healthy Schools* programmes

Provide local alcohol services

Ensure integrated service provision | Develop and implement *National Service Framework for Older People* |

A National Contract for Mental health	People can:	Local Players and Communities can:	Government and National Players can:
Social & Economic	Take opportunities to improve their education, training and employment Develop parenting skills Support friends at times of stress – be a good listener Participate in support and self-help groups Work to understand the needs of people with mental illness	Tackle inequity and social exclusion Work within health improvement programmes to develop local mental health initiatives on prevention, better identification and treatment, including help for at-risk groups such as recently bereaved, lone parents, unemployed people, refugees Develop job and volunteeering opportunities for people with mental illness Develop strategies to support the needs of mentally ill people from black and minority ethnic groups Encourage positive local media reporting to reduce stigma surrounding mental illness	Consider the mental health impact when developing policy on employment, education, social welfare, child abuse, children in care and leaving care, refugees and substance misuse Develop *New Deal for Communities* Tackle joblessness, and social exclusion Improve provision of mental health systems and collection of information Tackle alcohol and drug misuse Ensure responsible media reporting of suicide and homicides
Environmental	Improve workload management Support colleagues Visit elderly friends and family who are isolated Encourage children to read Encourage children to adopt a healthy diet and take physical activity Be alert to bullying at school Be alert to glue sniffing and substance misuse in schools Engage in regular parent-teacher dialogue Ensure children have safe access to public open space	Develop effective housing strategies which meet the needs of local communities Reduce stress in the workplace Develop local initiatives to reduce crime and violence and improve community safety Develop school programmes for mental health promotion including coping strategies, social supports and anti-bullying strategies, substance misuse detection and treatment Develop local programmes to tackle dyslexia in schools Encourage use of open spaces for leisure and social events	Continue to invest in housing, supported housing, to reduce discrimination and stigmatisation and reduce homelessness Encourage employers to develop workplace health policies which address mental health Reduce isolation through equitable transport policies Promote healthy schools and include mental as well as physical health education Promote healthy prisons and address mental illness in prisoners

A National Contract for Mental health	People can:	Local Players and Communities can:	Government and National Players can:
Personal behaviour	Use opportunities for relaxation and physical exercise and try to avoid using alcohol/smoking to reduce stress Increase understanding of what good mental health is Contribute to the creation of happy and healthy work and school environments	Support people with severe mental illness and ensure their access to other mainstream services for physical health as well as the mental health care they need	Increase public awareness and understanding of mental health and mental illness Reduce access to means of suicide Develop healthy living centres
Services	Contribute information to service planners and get involved Contact services quickly when difficulties start Increase knowledge about self-help	Develop range of comprehensive and culturally sensitive mental health services in accordance with *Modernising Mental Health Services* Implement the *National Service Framework for Mental Health* Provide advice and practical help on financial, housing, day care, and work problems	Develop the *National Service Framework for Mental Health* Provide incentives to emphasise good mental health care Audit all suicides and learn the lessons for prevention (the Confidential Inquiry into Suicide and Homicide)

Appendix 2

Our Healthier Nation White Paper – Glossary and References

Glossary and Technical Notes

National Targets – to reduce mortality from: cancer; coronary heart disease and stroke and related conditions; suicide; and to reduce the rate of fatal and serious injury from accidents.

Target year: 2010 for all four targets.

Baseline year:
Mortality targets: the average of the European age standardised rates for the three years 1995, 1996 and 1997.
Serious injury from accidents target: the hospital admission rates for the year 1995/96.

Sources of data:
Mortality targets: Office for National Statistics (ONS) mortality statistics from death registrations. Mortality rates are age standardised to allow for changes in the age structure of the population (using the European standard population as defined by the World Health Organisation).
Serious injury target: Hospital Episode Statistics.

Definitions:

Cancer – all malignant neoplasms – ICD-9 codes 140-208 inclusive.
Age group: under 75.
Target reduction by year 2010 – at least **one fifth (20%)**.

Coronary heart disease and stroke and related conditions – includes all circulatory diseases – International Classification of Diseases ICD-9 codes 390-459 inclusive.
Age group: under 75.
Target reduction by year 2010 – at least **two fifths (40%)**.

Accidents – mortality from accidents and adverse effects – ICD-9 codes E800-E949 inclusive
Age group: all ages
Target reduction by year 2010 – at least **one fifth (20%)**.

– serious accidental injury relating to hospital admissions defined by ICD-10 codes as below
Age group: all ages
Target reduction by year 2010 – at least **one tenth (10%)**.

The injury must be sufficiently serious to require a hospital stay of four days or more

Accident morbidity

- Primary diagnosis must indicate an injury, ie is in range S00 through T98X

- External cause code must be in one of the following ranges:
V01 – V99	Transport accidents
W00 – X59	Other external causes of accidental injury (mostly falls)
Y40 – Y84	Complications of medical and surgical care

- Length of stay must exceed 3 days.

As some records with a primary diagnosis indicating an injury do not contain a valid external cause code, these codes will be scaled out in proportion to the records with a valid cause code before applying the second rule above. Coding of external cause is consistently improving and this correction will decrease in importance as coding approaches 100%.

Suicide – suicide and undetermined injury – ICD-9 codes E950-E959 plus E980-E989 minus E988.8
Age group: all ages.
Target reduction by year 2010 – at least **one fifth (20%)**.

International Classification of Diseases

The World Health Organisation maintains a statistical classification of diseases, injuries and causes of death, which is internationally recognised and used. Currently, the ninth revision of this classification (ICD-9) is used in England for differentiating causes of death, but the tenth revision (ICD-10) is used for classifying hospital episodes.

Suicide and undetermined injury

Official suicides are those in which the coroner or official recorder has decided there is clear evidence that the injury was self-inflicted and the deceased intended to kill himself. Unofficial suicides or open verdicts are those where there may be doubt about the deceased's intentions. Research studies show that most open verdicts are in fact suicides. For the purposes of comparisons with other countries, the figures quoted are for official suicides, but for the purpose of measuring overall suicides in England, official suicides and open verdicts are combined.

Social class

The Registrar General's Social Class groupings used in this document are as follows:

	Social class grouping	Example occupations
I	Professional	Doctors, engineers
II	Managerial/technical	Managers, teachers
IIIN	Non-manual skilled	Clerks, cashiers
IIIM	Manual skilled	Carpenters, van drivers
IV	Partly skilled	Warehousemen, security guards
V	Unskilled	Labourers

It should be noted that the proportion of the working population falling into these groups changes over time, and comparisons of social class groupings over time should therefore be interpreted with caution.

Chapter Two
Fig no.   Description

2.1   **A major decline in death from all infectious diseases in the 20th Century**
Derived from: Office for National Statistics. Charlton J, Murphy M, eds. *The Health of Adult Britain: 1841-1994.* London: The Stationery Office, 1997. Additional data to 1997 from series DH2 nos 22,23,24. London: The Stationery Office, 1997, 1998, 1998.

2.2   **Major improvements in expectation of life after centuries of early death**
Office for National Statistics. Drever F, Whitehead M, eds. *Health Inequalities.* London: The Stationery Office, 1997.

2.3   **Major fall in infant deaths in the 20th century**
Office for National Statistics. *Mortality Statistics: Childhood, infant and perinatal (series DH1 no. 19 (1841-1985) and DH3).* London: The Stationery Office, DH1 - 1989, and DH3 - 1990-1998.

2.4   **Age at death at the start and end of the 20th century**
1900 The Registrar General. *Sixty-Third Annual Report of the Registrar General of Births, Deaths and Marriages in England, 1900.* London: HMSO, 1902.
1997 Office for National Statistics. *Mortality Statistics Cause, England and Wales 1997 (DH2 no.24).* London: The Stationery Office, 1998.

2.5   **Selected causes of death at the start, middle and end of this century**
1900 The Registrar General. *Sixty-Third Annual Report of the Registrar General of Births, Deaths and Marriages in England, 1900.* London: HMSO, 1902.
1950 Office for National Statistics. Charlton J, Murphy M, eds. *The Health of Adult Britain: 1841-1994.* London: The Stationery Office, 1997.
1997 Office for National Statistics. *Mortality Statistics Cause, England and Wales, 1997 (DH2 no.24).* London: The Stationery Office, 1998.

2.6   **Deaths before age 75 years in England annually: a major contribution from the four priority areas**
Based on : Department of Health. *Public Health Common Data Set, 1998.* (Derived from Office for National Statistics data). London: London School of Hygiene and Tropical Medicine, 1998.

2.7   **Unhealthy years at the end of life**
Bone M R, Bebbington A C, Jagger C, Morgan K, Nicolaas G. *Health Expectancy and Its Uses.* London: HMSO, 1995.

Chapter Three
Fig no.   Description

3.1   **Heart disease among public sector workers: higher rates associated with lack of control over job**
Bosma H, Marmot M, Hemingway H, Nicholson A, Brunner E, Stansfield S. Low job control and risk of coronary heart disease in Whitehall II (prospective cohort) study. *British Medical Journal* 1997; **314:** 558-565.

Chapter Four
Fig. no. Description

4.1   **Death and disadvantage: excess death rates amongst men in non-professional classes**
Office for National Statistics. Drever F, Whitehead M, eds. *Health Inequalities.* London: The Stationery Office, 1997.

4.2   **The widening mortality gap between social classes**
Office for National Statistics, Decennial Supplements, indexed by Department of Health Statistics Division 2.

4.3   **Asthmatics are two to three times more likely to live in damp properties**
Williamson I J, Martin C J, McGill G, Monie R D H, Fennerty A G. *Damp Housing and asthma: a case-control study. Thorax,* 1997; **52:** 229-234.

Chapter Five
Fig. no. Description

5.1   **Change in annual death rates: some improving, some worsening**
Analysed by Department of Health, Statistics Division 2, from Office for National Statistics data.

5.2   **Death rates from all cancers - England in the middle of the Western Europe rankings**
World Health Organisation, Copenhagen. Health For All indicators database (EU) England data analysed by Department of Health, Statistics Division 2 from Office for National Statistics data (ICD-9 140-208)

5.3   **Death rates from breast cancer: UK amongst the worst in Western Europe**
World Health Organisation, Copenhagen. Health For All indicators database (EU) England data analysed by Department of Health, Statistics Division 2, from Office for National Statistics data. (ICD-9 174)

5.4   **Death rates from cervical cancer: English women amongst worst in Western Europe**
World Health Organisation, Copenhagen. Health For All indicators database (EU) England data analysed by Department of Health, Statistics Division 2, from Office for National Statistics data. (ICD-9 180)

5.5   **Cancer survival: England and Wales generally lag behind Europe and USA**
Office for National Statistics. *Cancer Survival Trends in England and Wales 1971-1995. Deprivation and NHS Region.* London: The Stationery Office, 1999. (Includes data from Eurocare II (EU) and Seer (USA))

5.6   **Survival is better in affluent than in deprived areas**
Office for National Statistics. *Cancer Survival Trends in England and Wales 1971-1995. Deprivation and NHS Region.* London: The Stationery Office, 1999.

5.7   **Some spectacular breakthroughs: five year survival rates for acute lymphoblastic leukaemia in children.**
Cancer Research Campaign Factsheet 23.2 1995 and Office for National Statistics. *Cancer Survival Trends in England and Wales 1971-1995. Deprivation and NHS Region.* London: The Stationery Office, 1999.

5.8   **Ways of beating cancer: examples of how everyone can play their part**

Chapter Six
Fig no.   Description

6.1   **Death rates from circulatory disease: UK amongst highest in Western Europe**
World Health Organisation, Copenhagen. Health For All indicators database
(EU). (ICD-9 390-459)

6.2   **Death rates from stroke: English women one of the worst records in Western Europe**
World Health Organisation, Copenhagen. Health For All indicators database
(EU) England data analysed by Department of Health, Statistics Division 2, from
Office for National Statistics data. (ICD-9 430-438)

6.3   **Levels of smoking have fallen more quickly in professional classes**
Office for National Statistics. Series *General Household Survey (1972-1996).*
London: The Stationery Office 1974-1998.

6.4   **Obesity in women: higher levels amongst manual social groups**
Social and Community Planning Research (SCPR), Department of
Epidemiology and Public Health. Prescott-Clarke P, Primatesta P eds. *Health
Survey for England 1996.* London: The Stationery Office, 1998.

6.5   **Well under half of people with high blood pressure are treated successfully**
Social and Community Planning Research (SCPR), Department of
Epidemiology and Public Health. Prescott-Clarke P, Primatesta P eds. 1991-96
data from *Health Survey for England 1996.* London: The Stationery Office, 1998.
Data for *Health Survey for England 1997* published on Internet website:
www.doh.gov.uk/stats/hstab97/intro.htm

6.6   **Unequal risk of heart disease death at different employment levels in the public sector: even after allowing for risk factors**
Marmot M, Shipley M J, Rose G. Inequalities in death - specific explanations of
a general pattern? *The Lancet* 1984; **1;** 1003-1006.

6.7   **Differing rates of coronary bypass operations and angioplasties**
Department of Health, Hospital Episode Statistics data, calculated by Statistics
Division 2. Figures are provisional, no adjustments have been made for shortfalls
in data (i.e. the data are ungrossed).

6.8   **Ways of beating coronary heart disease and stroke: examples of how everyone can play their part**

Chapter Seven
Fig no.   Description

7.1   **Deaths from motor vehicle traffic accidents: England performs comparatively well**
World Health Organisation, Copenhagen. Health For All indicators database
(EU) England data analysed by Department of Health Statistics Division 2, from
Office for National Statistics data. (ICD-9 E810-E819)

7.2   **Death rates from all accidents in children**
England data analysed by Department of Health, Statistics Division 2, from
Office for National Statistics data.

7.3   **Child pedestrian deaths: England one of the worst records in Europe**
International Road Traffic and Accident database (OECD) via Department of the
Environment, Transport and the Regions. From website -
www.bast.de/indexeng.htm

7.4   Accidents kill proportionately more children as they grow up
Analysed by Department of Health, Statistics Division 2, from Office for National Statistics data

7.5   Deaths from accidental falls in older people are not reducing
Analysed by Department of Health, Statistics Division 2, from Office for National Statistics data.

7.6   Childhood accident deaths involving head injury occur close to home
Derived from Sharples P M, Storey A, Aynsley-Green A, Eyre J A. *British Medical Journal* 1990; **301:** 1193-7.

7.7   Traffic calming can cut pedestrian road accidents
Birmingham City Council via Birmingham Health Authority.

7.8   Ways of beating accidental injury: examples of how everyone can play their part

Chapter Eight
Fig no. Description

8.1   Death rates from suicide: England one of the best records in European Union
World Health Organisation, Copenhagen. Health For All indicators database (EU) England data analysed by Department of Health, Statistics Division 2, from Office for National Statistics data. (ICD-9 E950-E959).

8.2   Ways of beating mental health problems: examples of how everyone can play their part

Chapter Nine
Fig no. Description

9.1   Live births to teenage women in Europe: UK has the highest rate in Western Europe
Eurostat and United Nations Demographic Yearbook 1996, via Social Exclusion Unit.

9.2   Underage pregnancies: a map of inequalities
Based on: Department of Health. *Public Health Common Data Set, 1998.* (Derived from Office for National Statistics data). London: London School of Hygiene and Tropical Medicine, 1998.

9.3   Percentage of young males and females who have taken illicit drugs
Ramsay M, Spiller J, *Drug Misuse Declared in 1996: Latest Results from the British Crime Survey.* Home Office Research Study no 172. London: Home Office, 1997.

9.4   Some of the most common adverse health effects of heavy alcohol consumption
Department of Health. Based on *Sensible drinking. The report of an inter-departmental working group.* Department of Health, 1995

9.5   The rising trend of reports of food poisoning
Public Health Laboratory Service, website - www.phls.co.uk/facts/foodt1.htm

9.6   Vaccination conquers disease: the trend for diphtheria
Derived from: Office for National Statistics. Charlton J, Murphy M, eds. *The Health of Adult Britain: 1841-1994.* London: The Stationery Office, 1997. Additional data to 1997: Public Health Laboratory Service, website - www.phls.co.uk/facts/dip.htm

9.7 **An old adversary returning: the recent rise in tuberculosis**
Public Health Laboratory Service, website - www.phls.co.uk/facts/tube-toi.htm

9.8 **Women in some ethnic groups have a low uptake of potentially life-saving cervical cancer smears**
Health Education Authority. Kai Rudat ed. of MORI Health Research Unit. *Black and Minority Ethnic Groups in England. Health and Lifestyles.* Great Britain: BPC Wheatons Ltd; 1994.

9.9 **Relative mortality from coronary heart disease by ethnic origin**
Wild S, McKeigue P: *British Medical Journal* **314,** (7082) 1997: 705-710, from Office for National Statistics data.

9.10 **High rates of suicide amongst young women born in the Indian sub-continent and living in this country**
Soni Raleigh V. Suicide patterns and trends in people of Indian Subcontinent and Caribbean origin in England and Wales. *Ethnicity and Health,* 1996:**1**(1): 55-63.

Chapter Eleven
Fig no. Description

11.1 Cancers: how the strategy will save lives

11.2 Circulatory disease: how the strategy will save lives

11.3 Accidental injury: how the strategy will save lives

11.4 Suicide: how the strategy will save lives

Estimates by Department of Health Economics and Operational Research Division, based on mortality data from Office for National Statistics.

Printed in the UK for The Stationery Office Limited
on behalf of the Controller of Her Majesty's Stationery Office
Dd 5068896   7/99   61743   Job No J0084986